INTRODUCING GEOLOGY: 5

EDITOR: J. A. G. THOMAS
Head of Geography and Geology Department,
Verdin Comprehensive School, Winsford, Cheshire

C000271174

Fieldwork in Geology

I. M. SIMPSON, B.Sc., Ph.D.
Senior Lecturer in Stratigraphy, University of Manchester

London
A THOMAS MURBY PUBLICATION OF
GEORGE ALLEN & UNWIN
Boston   Sydney

FIRST PUBLISHED IN 1977

Filmset in Monophoto Baskerville Series 169
Printed Offset Litho in Great Britain by Cox & Wyman Ltd,
London, Fakenham and Reading

PREFACE

This book is intended to be of use to all those who are beginning to experience the joys, and the frustrations, of geological fieldwork. It is assumed that the readers will have no more than an elementary knowledge of the basic facts and theories of geology, but will be willing and able to go to suitable areas and examine the rock exposures for themselves. If it helps to instil in its readers some awareness of the vital part that geology plays in shaping and controlling the environment in which we live, this book will have succeeded.

The author is greatly indebted to his family, his friends, and his colleagues at the University of Manchester for their patience and help. To Mr J. A. G. Thomas and Mr F. G. Goodwin, who critically read the manuscript and suggested many improvements, the author is particularly grateful. The Geologists' Association readily granted permission to include substantial parts of their *Code for Geological Field Work* on the back cover of this book. The importance of strict adherence to this code by all field workers in geology cannot be too highly stressed.

I. M. S.

TABLES

CONTENTS

1
Introduction

THE study of rocks, minerals and fossils in their natural environment in the field is one of the most fundamental and enjoyable parts of the science of geology. When a geologist undertakes a field survey of an area, perhaps in a search for useful resources such as coal or iron ore, or perhaps to determine a possible route for a new motorway, or, more likely, just to find out what is there, he begins by carefully examining all the natural exposures of rock in the area. He would expect to find most of the exposures in places where active erosion of the land surface is taking place. The steeper parts of hillsides, the banks of swiftly flowing rivers and streams, coastal cliffs and rocky headlands often provide good exposures. Artificial or man-made exposures, such as quarries, mines, road and railway cuttings, would also be examined once permission to visit them has been obtained.

At each exposure the geologist has to determine which kinds of rocks and minerals are present, which types of structure are displayed by the rocks, and whether or not they contain identifiable fossils. If the rocks display well defined bedding layers or, in other words, are well stratified, he measures the thicknesses of the individual layers (Fig. 1.1). If, as is usually the case, the layers are inclined, he measures the angle of inclination with a simple instrument known as a clinometer (Fig. 1.2). This angle, which is measured relative to the horizontal, is called the dip of the beds and it provides the geologist with important clues regarding the nature of any folding which the rocks may have undergone. As it is also important to know the exact direction in which the rocks are dipping, an accurate measurement of this direction is made with a magnetic compass.

Other important structural features observed in rocks in the field include faults, joints and cleavage. Faults are caused by fracture and displacement of the

Figure 1.1   Measuring the thickness of beds of sandstone with a measuring tape; note that the thickness is measured perpendicular to the bedding planes.

Figure 1.2   Measuring the angle of dip of a bed of sandstone with a compass-clinometer.

rocks (Fig. 1.3). If the exposure is good the amount of displacement and direction of movement of a fault can be measured. Joints are cracks in rocks caused by pressure or tension acting on the rocks at some time in the past. Very often they show a fairly regular pattern of development (Fig. 1.4). Measurement of the directions in which the joints run can provide important evidence regarding the nature of the forces which acted on the rocks to produce the joints.

Some rocks, such as slate and schist, have a distinct tendency to split readily in a preferred direction (Fig. 1.5). This property, which results from intense

Figure 1.3   A vein of microgranite (light) intruded into diorite (dark) at Sorel Point, Jersey; the vein has been broken by a small fault and displaced about one metre.

Figure 1.4   A fairly regular pattern of jointing displayed by the granite at Sorel Point, Jersey.

Figure 1.5   The characteristic cleavage of slate; the block is 20 cm long and the bedding is at 45° towards the bottom left-hand corner.

pressure on the rocks, is known as cleavage and is an important field characteristic whose direction and inclination can be measured with compass and clinometer.

In order that an accurate record of all the measurements and observations made by the field geologist can be kept he makes detailed notes in his field note-book at each locality visited. He also plots on a detailed map of the area the precise position of all the rock outcrops together with the directions and amounts of dip of strata, the directions of cleavage, joints, faults and any other significant features which he has observed. Construction of this, the field map, is perhaps the most demanding aspect of geological fieldwork and, when done properly, it requires considerable skill and patience.

During the course of fieldwork in geology it is often necessary to collect representative specimens of the rocks, minerals and fossils for more detailed examination later. How this can be done without causing too much damage to the environment and offence to other users of the countryside will be described in a later chapter.

Most of the equipment needed for geological fieldwork is simple and inex-pensive. A notebook, map, hammer, chisel, magnifying lens and measuring tape are standard items. For accurate field-mapping a magnetic compass and a clino-meter, either separate or combined in one instrument, the compass–clinometer, are essential. A full description of these instruments and how to use them follows in the next chapter. The other essential items cannot be bought. They are a keen pair of eyes and a flair for observing the finer details of all aspects of the landscape.

The rocks which are exposed at the earth's surface are the field geologist's principal laboratory. By carefully observing, measuring and recording all the data obtainable from the rocks, he is gathering clues which enable him to construct a three-dimensional model of the crustal structure of a region. The accuracy of this model is limited partly by the fact that in most areas only a very small fraction of the rocks of the crust is exposed, and hence the number of clues is restricted, and partly by the accuracy of the geologist's own observations. As in any other branch of scientific research, the standard method in geological fieldwork is to gather as many observations and measurements as are available and from these make deductions and put forward theories and hypotheses which are subsequently tested by other researchers. The emphasis throughout is on accurate observation and measurement.

You do not have to be an expert to be able to enjoy geological fieldwork. Even the complete beginner, knowing little of the more elaborate theories of geology, such as the origin of the earth, the evolution of plants and animals, and the movements of crustal plates, can get a great deal of pleasure and excitement from fieldwork. By picking up a pebble from a beach, or a fallen rock from an old quarry, splitting them open and finding inside a fossil ammonite or some fine crystals of quartz, you are exploring parts of our planet upon which no other human being has ever set his eyes. That is what geology is all about.

2

Equipment for Fieldwork in Geology
TOPOGRAPHICAL MAPS

THE two most important things a geologist working in the field needs to know are (a) exactly where he or she is at any particular moment, and (b) exactly where the rock exposures are. A good topographical map of the area is therefore an essential item of equipment. In Britain the best maps for the purpose are published by the Ordnance Survey. They are issued in a variety of scales, those most commonly used by geologists being the 1:50000, 1:25000 and 1:10000 series. Occasionally it is necessary to use maps on the much larger scales of 1:2500 and 1:1250 for very detailed field projects.

Each sheet of the 1:50000 series of maps covers an area 40 km square and shows all the major natural topographical features in the area along with the towns, villages, roads, railways, footpaths and other man-made landmarks. These maps are very useful for route planning and could also be used for the more general type of field survey, but they have the disadvantage of being drawn on such a small scale (one kilometre on the ground is represented by only two centimetres on the map) that few of the minor details of the topography can be shown.

For detailed geological mapping the 1:10000 series is the most useful. Each map of this series covers an area five km square. There are no distracting colours on these maps and there is normally plenty of space (one kilometre on the ground is represented by ten centimetres on the map) to allow the insertion of the location of rock exposures, dip measurements and other geological data in a clear, legible and accurate form.

GEOLOGICAL MAPS

Many of the Ordnance Survey maps are issued overprinted with geological information compiled by the Institute of Geological Sciences. These are very useful in fieldwork, especially if the object is simply to visit an area to see what is there and to collect suitable specimens. Among the several types of geological maps issued the most generally useful are the coloured 'drift' and 'solid' maps on the 1:50000 and 1:25000 scales.

Drift deposits consist mainly of clays, sands, gravels and peats of Glacial and Post-Glacial age and occur at shallow depth in layers rarely more than a few metres thick. The drift map shows what is thought would be seen if all the vegetation and soil were removed from the area so as to expose the top surface of the drift deposits in those parts in which they occur, and the top surface of the underlying, older, consolidated rocks in those parts where drift deposits are absent.

The solid map shows what it is believed would be seen if, in addition to the vegetation and soil, most of the drift deposits with the exception of recent alluvium and peat were stripped away to expose the surface of the consolidated rocks. The advantage of the solid map is that it provides a clearer representation of the geological structure of the older rocks, but the drift edition of a map is a better guide to what you will actually see when you visit the area.

In lowland regions, particularly in the northern half of the British Isles, the drift deposits are extensive so that there are considerable differences between the solid and drift editions of maps of such areas. The maps in Figure 2.1 have been adapted from the solid and drift editions of the 1:50000 scale Geological Survey map of an area near Alnwick in Northumberland which has an extensive drift cover. They illustrate how important it is when buying a geological map to specify

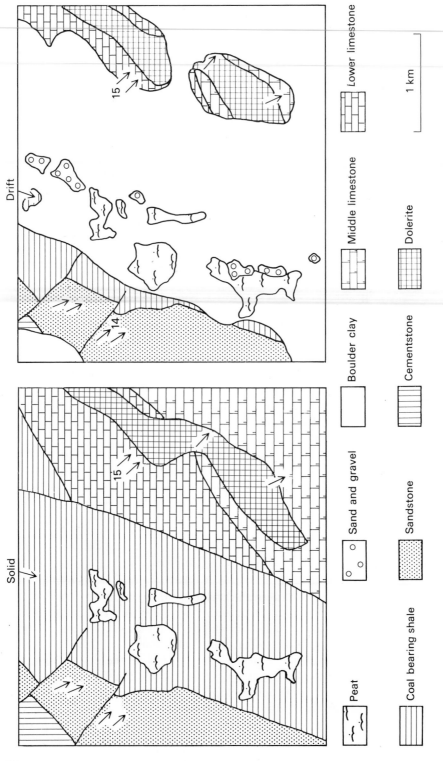

Figure 2.1 Solid and drift maps of the same area; based on Geological Survey map Sheet 6 (1 : 50 000 Alnwick district), reproduced by permission of the Controller, Her Majesty's Stationery Office. Crown copyright.

whether it is the solid or the drift edition that is required. A catalogue listing the availability of topographical and geological maps along with details of where they can be obtained is published by the Ordnance Survey (see Appendix, p. 70).

HAMMERS AND CHISELS

A geologist without a hammer is in a similar position to a referee without a whistle. Both the hammer and the whistle are simple and effective pieces of equipment, but the good geologist uses his hammer sparingly, as does the good referee his whistle.

Typically a geological hammer has a tough steel head one end of which is wedge-shaped and used for digging out loose boulders, clearing away soil and sand from around rock exposures and the final trimming of rock and mineral specimens. The other end of the head is square and is used to detach pieces of rock from solid outcrops and to break boulders up into smaller fragments. Ideally the hammer should weigh about a half to one kilogram; anything lighter than this is ineffective against most of the common rocks. Occasionally a heavier hammer may be required to break very tough rocks like granite, but to carry an extra-heavy hammer in the field all day can be tiresome and is generally not worth the effort.

To hammer rocks successfully a certain knack is required and it can only be learnt by experience. A direct, frontal attack on a rocky outcrop or a large, smooth boulder usually results in nothing more than sore hands, stinging fingers and, perhaps, a broken hammer. It is much better to select carefully a protruding edge or sharp corner of rock and with a deft, wristy swing of the hammer give it a hard, sharp blow with the edge of the square face (Fig. 2.2). With very hard rocks several blows of the hammer may be required, and in such cases the point of attack on the rock should be varied from blow to blow in order to weaken the rock gradually and allow cracks to develop. In order to protect the head of the hammer from uneven wear and tear, successive blows should be aimed from different angles, thus ensuring that different parts of the head come into contact with the

Figure 2.2   Obtaining a specimen of sandstone from an outcrop; note that the rock is being hammered at its weakest point.

Figure 2.3   Trimming a small specimen to the desired shape and size by using the wedge-shaped end of the geological hammer.

rock. If the same part of the head were used every time it would soon wear away and become blunt and ineffective.

Some safety precautions should be taken when hammering. It is important that the head of the hammer should be made of steel tempered to the correct degree of hardness. If the steel is too soft the head will rapidly wear away; if too brittle, as in most ordinary hammers, sharp splinters may fly off in use and cause painful injuries. A similar problem arises when hammering hard, splintery rocks such as flint, quartzite and rhyolite. Razor-sharp fragments can fly off in unpredictable directions and may cause nasty cuts. It is prudent, therefore, when hammering such rocks to wear protective gloves and eye-goggles, to warn others to stand clear, and to use only a hammer designed specifically for geological use.

Trimming rough specimens down to the size and shape desired for a collection also calls for some skill and judgement. Specimens which are neither particularly hard nor too heavy can be held in the hand while being trimmed (Fig. 2.3). The sharp wedge end of the head is usually more useful for trimming than the square end, especially if the specimen has any tendency to split along a bedding plane or a cleavage plane. Larger specimens, too heavy to be held in the hand, can be split and trimmed by being held steady on the ground under the toe of your boot while being hammered (Fig. 2.4). Needless to say, for the sake of your specimens and your toes, this should be done very carefully. When trimmed a specimen should be roughly rectangular in shape and have clean, fresh, unweathered faces free from any signs of crushing and powdering by the hammer. Quite a lot of practice is needed to achieve this.

The main object of hammering is to obtain specimens needed for further study in the laboratory or for adding to a collection. When you come to an exposure of rock that you wish to examine you should always think twice before starting to hammer it. Consider carefully whether it is really necessary to hammer the rock at all. Very often by simply looking closely at the rocks you will learn all that you really need to know. If you must have a specimen for your collection see if there are any loose blocks of the rock lying about which could be broken up in

Figure 2.4   Trimming a large specimen to the desired shape and size; the weathered and discoloured portions of the rock are being removed.

preference to disfiguring the weathered face of a natural outcrop. It would be better still just to take a photograph. By so doing you will avoid antagonising the many farmers and landowners who have in the past been troubled by geologists hammering indiscriminately at rocks on their land. It is worth remembering that because of the destruction caused by the unnecessary hammering of rocks several interesting areas are now banned to geologists, while in other places the outcrops have been so hammered out of recognition that they are no longer worth visiting. The geologist's code of conduct (see the back cover of this book) should be strictly followed at all times.

The geological hammer is necessarily a crude, blunt instrument designed for breaking up hard, resistant rocks. For more precise work, such as the extraction of delicate fossils or fragile minerals in an undamaged state, it is much more effective to cut the desired specimen out of its enclosing rock by means of a cold chisel. A steel chisel of the type used by stonemasons and measuring about 15 cm long and 1 or 2 cm wide is about right for most purposes. In order to extract specimens successfully much patience is needed and also some skill. There are several wrong ways and one correct way of going about it. Look carefully at Figure 2.5 and consider whether the fossil ammonite is likely to come cleanly out of the rock all in one piece, or if it will end up as a handful of useless, broken fragments. There are at least three reasons why the latter is the more likely to happen. In the first place both the rock and the fossil are already in a badly cracked condition, and this will only get worse as the chiselling proceeds. Secondly, the chiselling is being done so close to the fossil that it will be damaged. Thirdly, by directing the chisel inwards towards the fossil the probability of the rock flaking off in that direction and causing damage to the fossil is greatly increased.

Now study Figure 2.6. Here the rock is in a much sounder state to start with, the cut is being made at a safe distance away from the fossil and the chisel is being directed away from it, so that there is a reasonable chance that it will come out cleanly.

Figure 2.5   Extracting an ammonite from Jurassic shale at Raasay; in this case the chance of successfully extracting the fossil is small.

Figure 2.6   Extracting another ammonite from shale, this time with more likelihood of success, but, for this specimen, hardly worth the effort.

It is, of course, much easier to chisel fossil and mineral specimens out of relatively soft rocks, such as chalk and mudstone, than out of hard, brittle rocks like slate. The same rules apply, however, whatever the rock, and with the harder rocks even more patience is required.

MAGNIFYING LENSES

A magnifying lens is a very useful tool for examining mineral grains in rocks, small crystals of minerals, and the finer details of fossils. If you collect postage stamps you may already have a lens that would be suitable for geology. If not, a cheap and relatively easy lens to use is the type shown in Figure 2.7. It consists

Figure 2.7   Viewing quartz crystals through the lens of a cheap, illuminating magnifier.

of a lens of clear plastic which magnifies the specimen about two times. Built into the handle of the instrument is a small torch which illuminates the relatively wide field of view and gives a very clear view of the specimen.

A more professional but, unfortunately, much more expensive instrument is the small glass lens whose method of use is illustrated in Figure 2.8. This type of lens normally has a magnification of about eight or ten times and this, combined with the rather small field of view, makes it quite difficult to use. When examining

Figure 2.8   Examining a specimen with an $8\times$ hand-lens; note that the lens is held close to the eye and the sharp focus is obtained by adjusting the position of the specimen.

a specimen with this type of lens always remember to (a) hold the lens steady and close up to your eye, (b) position yourself so that the source of light is above and behind you in order to illuminate the specimen, and (c) focus by moving the specimen, not the lens, to the correct distance. A little practice is necessary in learning to use this type of lens successfully.

MEASURING TAPES AND RULERS

The measuring tape is used to determine the thickness of beds in stratified deposits and the width of mineral veins, dykes and sills. The most convenient type for general use is the flexible stainless steel tape which can be extended up to 2 metres, but, when not in use, can be rolled back into a small container no more than 5 cm across (Fig. 1.1). If funds do not permit a measuring tape an ordinary ruler would do almost as well. An even more simple measuring device, accurate enough for most purposes, can be made by painting marks or cutting small notches at 1 cm intervals along the length of the handle of your hammer.

In field mapping, in order to plot the exact position of outcrops, it is often necessary to measure distances of tens or even hundreds of metres with a fair degree of accuracy. Professional surveyors use measuring tapes which extend to 20 m or more, but a cheaper, if slightly less accurate, method is to pace out the distance on the ground. Knowing the length of his average pace, as every good field geologist should, it is a matter of simple arithmetic to convert the number of paces to metres.

CLINOMETERS AND COMPASSES

The clinometer is used to measure the angles at which strata dip relative to the horizontal. Anyone making a detailed geological map of stratified deposits will find it essential to have a clinometer as it is only by accurately measuring the angles of dip that the nature of many of the structures can be determined.

As clinometers are quite expensive instruments to buy it is worth considering making one for yourself. All that is needed is a plastic protractor, a rectangular piece of plywood or similar material, a short piece of strong thread or fine cord (nylon fishing-line is ideal), a small weight and some glue. The plywood should measure about 15 cm by 20 cm, and it is important that it should be exactly rectangular.

The first step in making the clinometer is to glue the protractor to the plywood so that its straight edge is exactly parallel with the shorter edges of the plywood and at right angles to the longer edges. A small hole is then bored through the centre point of the semicircular scale of the protractor and through the plywood backing. The thread is then passed through the hole and a knot tied at the back to keep it in place. The small weight is tied to the other end of the thread so that it hangs just below the curved edge of the protractor. The weight acts as a plumb-line so that by placing the clinometer with one of its longer edges along the maximum slope of the inclined surface of a bedding plane the angle of dip can be measured directly from the scale (Fig. 2.9). With a little care in construction this home-made clinometer is every bit as accurate as the manufactured article, and it is much cheaper.

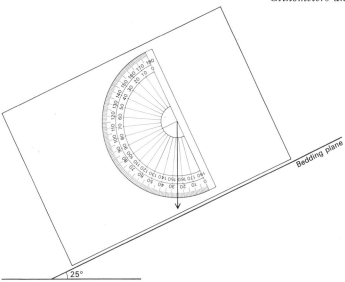

Figure 2.9 A clinometer which you can make for yourself from a plastic protractor and some plywood.

The Silva compass–clinometer consists of an oilfilled compass of the kind used in hill walking and orienteering, with a built-in clinometer of the weighted pointer type (Fig. 2.10). To measure the angle of dip of an inclined bed lay the long flat edge of the compass–clinometer on the surface of the inclined bed so that it is aligned in the direction of maximum slope of the bed and the pointer is hanging free. The angle of dip of the bed is then read off on the graduated scale of the instrument. Finally, the direction in which the bed is dipping is determined by use of the compass.

Figure 2.10 The Silva compass–clinometer: the pointer with the diamond-shaped head registers the angle of dip of the bed upon which the instrument rests: in this case the angle is 25°.

CLOTHING, FOOTWEAR, ETC.

Crossing rough country in bad weather is a hazard frequently experienced in geological fieldwork. Waterproof clothing and boots are therefore strongly recommended. A brightly coloured anorak (so that you can be easily spotted if you are lost) and an extra jersey should be carried in mountainous areas along with a whistle and some extra food in case of emergency. The choice of boots is very much a matter of personal preference. Some wear commando-type boots with thick, ribbed soles, others prefer heavy Wellingtons of the kind used by fishermen. High-heeled shoes with thin, slippery soles are absolutely useless in the field. Each day before setting off to do fieldwork make sure that somebody knows where you are to be working and at what time you expect to get back to your base, so that if there is an accident or if you get lost help can reach you as quickly as possible.

3

The Identification of Minerals in the Field

INTRODUCTION

THE finding of a really good mineral specimen is one of the most exciting things that can happen when you are doing geological fieldwork. Even if the mineral is a comparatively common one, like quartz or calcite, the thrill of unearthing a specimen bearing a really fine group of crystals is something to remember. Identifying the minerals may, however, prove more troublesome than the finding of them since there are several thousand different species of minerals known to occur in nature and few geologists would be sufficiently expert to identify in the field more than a small fraction of the total. Most minerals require a detailed microscopic examination and perhaps also a laboratory analysis before they can be precisely identified.

Fortunately for the ordinary field geologist only about thirty of the minerals are common enough and important enough to require immediate recognition in the field. These include the principal rock-forming minerals, like the feldspars and the micas, which occur in such enormously large quantities that they are major and essential components of many of the most common rocks of the earth's crust. Granite, for example, is a rock composed essentially of a mixture of minerals of the feldspar group, the mica group and quartz. To identify a rock as granite the geologist must therefore first identify these major component minerals.

The list of common rock-forming minerals whose diagnostic field characteristics will be described later in this chapter includes quartz, orthoclase feldspar, plagioclase feldspar, muscovite mica, biotite mica, hornblende, augite, olivine, chlorite, epidote, calcite, dolomite, garnet and tourmaline. There will also be descriptions of the field characteristics of some of the vein and ore minerals which, although much less common than the rock-forming minerals, are reasonably abundant, locally, in various parts of the British Isles. They include pyrite, chalcopyrite, malachite, azurite, hematite, magnetite, limonite, cassiterite, galena, sphalerite, fluorite, gypsum and barite.

FIELD IDENTIFICATION

The properties which are used to distinguish one mineral from another are (a) the chemical composition, and (b) various physical characters, such as colour, hardness, crystal symmetry, etc. Obviously it would not be feasible to make a chemical analysis of a mineral in the field, so spot identification depends largely on recognising a distinctive physical property or combination of properties for each common mineral (for a detailed description of the principal diagnostic properties see *Rocks and Minerals* (Introducing Geology series: 4) by Professor Janet Watson).

The physical properties most easily tested in the field are listed in Table 3.1. It should be noted that for any given mineral it is rare for one single property to prove absolutely diagnostic. In most cases positive identification depends upon recognition of a distinctive combination of several properties. To take an example, the mineral fluorite, which belongs to the cubic system, tends to display, if conditions are favourable, crystals which are in the form of nearly perfect cubes (Fig. 3.6). This, however, is not a diagnostic property because not only do many other minerals show a similar cubic form but it can also happen, occasionally, that fluorite will grow in a different form of the cubic system, such as the octahedron. The cubes, therefore, are a clue towards, but not conclusive evidence of, the identity of fluorite.

Table 3.1   *Physical properties used to identify minerals in the field*

---

1   *Crystal form.* The characteristic shape of the crystals depending on whether the mineral belongs to the cubic, tetragonal, orthorhombic, monoclinic, triclinic or hexagonal systems.

2   *Crystal habit.* The manner in which the crystals grow. The habit may be flaky, fibrous, needle-like, prismatic, pyramidal, etc. If the mineral is simply a mass of small, shapeless crystals, the habit is described as massive.

3   *Cleavage.* The property which some minerals have of being able to split readily in one or more preferred directions when broken, so producing flat, regular surfaces. The shape of the cleavage fragment can be a characteristic feature of some minerals. Other minerals, showing no cleavage, break with a curved or irregular surface known as the *fracture*.

4   *Colour.* This property can be diagnostic for some minerals, but in other cases the colour may be so variable, due to defects in the structure of the crystals or traces of impurities, as to be of little value in identification.

5   *Lustre.* The way in which the mineral reflects light. The lustre may be glassy, diamond-like, metallic, etc. The lustre of many minerals becomes dull after prolonged exposure to the weather. It is important, therefore, to examine freshly exposed surfaces of the mineral when determining its lustre.

6   *Hardness.* In the field this can be roughly determined by using a fingernail and a hammer. A soft mineral (grades 1 and 2 on the hardness scale) can be scratched by your fingernail (hardness 2·5); minerals in the medium range of hardness (i.e. 3, 4 or 5 on the scale) can be scratched by the steel head of your hammer or a penknife blade (hardness about 5·5), but not by your fingernail; minerals of hardness 6 or greater are not scratched by steel.

7   *Density.* A rough estimate can be made in the field by simply weighing a sample of the mineral in your hand. With a little practice it is relatively easy to distinguish any mineral that is either unusually heavy or unusually light.

8   *Magnetism.* A positive result to the magnetism test is obtained if a mineral causes an abnormal deflection to the needle of your compass when brought close up to it. Only one of the common minerals is magnetic.

A further clue is provided by an unusual habit that cubes of fluorite commonly have of apparently interfering with one another's growth, so that the corner of one cube can often be seen to be protruding from the face of another cube. This habit of interpenetrating growth is not, however, unique to fluorite crystals, nor is it always shown by fluorite. Very commonly the mineral occurs in a granular, massive habit without showing any obvious traces of its cubic structure, and when this occurs positive identification is very difficult.

The cleavage of fluorite is very good in four directions cutting obliquely across the corners of the cube, thus producing triangular cleavage faces. Fluorite can, in fact, be cleaved into a perfect octahedron with the eight triangular faces corresponding to the eight corners of the original cube. This rather unusual cleavage is the most distinctive property of fluorite. Colour, on the other hand, is too variable to be of any significance in identification, except perhaps in the purple and white colour-zoned variety. The lustre, which is glassy, has nothing particularly distinctive about it, nor has the hardness of 4 and the density of 3·2.

To summarise, a positive identification of fluorite depends mainly upon the recognition of interpenetrating cubes and octahedral cleavage. In a specimen consisting of large, well-grown crystals both these properties could be fairly obvious, making identification an easy matter. If, however, the specimen consists of a mass of small, shapeless, granular crystals, as happens only too often, identification in the field is very difficult indeed.

Using the properties listed in Table 3.1 as a guide to identification, we can now turn to the common minerals and determine which properties are of most use to help us recognise these minerals in the field.

Figure 3.1   A crystal of quartz showing the characteristic hexagonal prism capped by a hexagonal pyramid.

QUARTZ

Oxygen and silicon, by far the most abundant elements in the earth's crust, combine easily to form quartz. Consequently the mineral is exceedingly common, occurring not only in many igneous, metamorphic and sedimentary rocks (e.g. granite, quartzite and sandstone) but also in veins and cavities within these rocks. Furthermore, because the mineral displays so many variations in grain size, colour and habit, there are numerous named varieties of quartz (Table 3.2).

When growth is in the form of large, well-shaped crystals the hexagonal structure of the mineral is obvious (Fig. 3.1). The hardness of quartz is 7, the lustre is glassy, and the colour, although very variable, is commonly milky-white. Quartz has no cleavage, but breaks rather like glass to give smoothly curved surfaces. This type of fracture is known as conchoidal. In many veins the habit of the mineral is massive, with no visible signs of the hexagonal crystal form.

At first sight common quartz might be mistaken for calcite, but the greatly superior hardness of quartz and lack of cleavage are the distinguishing features. The amethyst variety of quartz is similar in colour to the purple form of fluorite, but again the greater hardness and the lack of cleavage of the quartz are distinctive.

In granite and granitic gneiss, where quartz forms part of the groundmass of the rock, it usually occurs as small, grey, irregularly-shaped, glassy crystals which are a good deal less conspicuous than the larger, opaque, white or pink crystals of feldspar and the shiny flakes of mica which, along with the quartz, make up the bulk of the rock.

Quartz in the form of detrital grains is the dominant constituent of most sandstones and it imparts a gritty feel to the rocks. Pebbles of quartz are very common in conglomerate.

The compact varieties of quartz are composed of crystals so small that a high-powered microscope is needed to see them individually. The hexagonal form of the crystals cannot be seen, even under the microscope, so that identification again depends mainly on the hardness and the conchoidal fracture.

Irregularly-shaped cavities, known as drusy cavities, are common in some granites (e.g. the Mourne Mountains granite), and such cavities are frequently

Table 3.2 *Common varieties of quartz*

Variety	Habit	Colour
common quartz	crystalline or massive	milky-white, opaque
rock crystal	crystalline	colourless, transparent
amethyst	crystalline or massive	purple, transparent or translucent
smoky quartz	crystalline	dark brown, transparent or translucent
citrine	crystalline	yellow, transparent
rose quartz	massive	pink, translucent
chalcedony	compact, microcrystalline	pale grey, translucent
agate	compact, microcrystalline	concentric bands of grey and brown, opaque or translucent
cornelian	compact, microcrystalline	yellow or red, translucent
jasper	compact, microcrystalline	dark red, opaque
flint	compact, microcrystalline	grey or brown, opaque
chert	compact, microcrystalline	dark grey or black, opaque

lined with crystals of quartz. Citrine and amethyst occur in this way in some of the Channel Islands granites and large crystals of smoky quartz have been found in drusy cavities in the Cairngorm granite, hence an alternative name for this variety is cairngorm.

The small, spherical cavities known as vesicles, which commonly occur in extrusive volcanic rocks as a result of the lava frothing and bubbling at the time it solidified, often at some later stage become partly or completely filled with quartz crystals. Small crystals of amethyst, for example, are common in the vesicles of the basalt at Calton Hill in north Derbyshire. Agate, chalcedony, cornelian and jasper are also common in vesicles.

Flint occurs in the form of irregular nodules in the chalky limestones of Upper Cretaceous age in many parts of Europe including the British Isles. Chert is very similar to flint but occurs mainly in older rocks, particularly in the Lower Carboniferous limestones of England and Wales and the Durness Limestone of north-west Scotland.

ORTHOCLASE FELDSPAR

This is a silicate of aluminium, potassium and sodium. Sometimes it also contains a little iron. It is common in some igneous and metamorphic rocks. In the so-called alkaline igneous rocks, which include syenites, trachytes and many granites, orthoclase is a major constituent in the form of clearly defined, brick-shaped crystals. In the 'big feldspar' granites of south-west England these crystals can be up to 15 cm in length (Fig. 3.2).

Orthoclase is usually light in colour, varying from white to creamy yellow and pink. Oxidation of the small iron content gives a deeper reddish-brown colour in some cases. It is almost always opaque with a dull to glassy lustre. The hardness is 6, slightly harder than steel.

Orthoclase crystals have two good directions of cleavage at right angles to one another. A characteristic feature of the crystals is a simple twinning resulting from the growth of the crystal taking place in such a way that one half of the atomic lattice of the crystal is reversed with respect to the other half. The twinning is

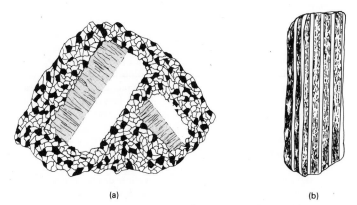

(a)

(b)

Figure 3.2 The typical twinning of feldspar crystals: (a) simple twinning of orthoclase in a porphyritic granite; (b) multiple twinning in plagioclase.

most obvious on freshly broken crystals where one half of the twin shows a smooth, shiny cleavage plane and the other half shows a dull, irregular fracture. On a sunny day such twins are conspicuous on exposed granite surfaces, e.g. the cliffs at Land's End in Cornwall.

Orthoclase can be distinguished from quartz by its good cleavage, from plagioclase by its simple twinning and from the other common light-coloured minerals by its superior hardness.

PLAGIOCLASE FELDSPAR

Plagioclase is the name given to a group of minerals composed of oxygen, silicon, aluminium, sodium and calcium, with the sodium and calcium interchangeable with one another, so that there is a complete range of plagioclases from sodium-rich at one extreme to calcium-rich at the other. The sodium-rich plagioclases are major components of the more acid (i.e. granitic) igneous rocks, while the calcium-rich plagioclases dominate in the more basic igneous rocks such as gabbro and basalt.

Plagioclase crystals often form part of the granular groundmass of the rock in which they occur and thus they tend to be less conspicuous than the larger and better-formed orthoclase crystals. Their colour is usually white or light grey, translucent or opaque and the lustre dull to glassy. The hardness is about 6·5, slightly harder than steel.

Plagioclase crystals have two good cleavages making an angle of about 86° with one another. This angle is too close to that of the cleavages in orthoclase to be of any use as a distinguishing factor in the field. The twinning, however, is a much more definitive feature, since, in contrast to the simple twinning of orthoclase, a multiple twinning is the rule in plagioclase. Each crystal is built up from numerous thin, parallel layers whose atomic structure alternates so that every second layer is reversed so far as its crystal properties are concerned. This multiple twinning is very obvious when a plagioclase crystal is examined with a polarising microscope, but in the field it is rather more difficult to detect. With a little practice, however, in catching the reflection of sunlight at just the correct angle, a freshly cleaved surface of plagioclase can be seen to have a finely striped appearance. The stripes are due to the alternating shiny and dull layers of the multiple twin (Fig. 3.2).

Plagioclase is distinguished from quartz by its cleavage, from orthoclase by its multiple twinning, and from the other common, lightly coloured minerals by its superior hardness.

MUSCOVITE MICA

Muscovite is a compound of oxygen, silicon, aluminium, potassium and hydrogen. Its habit is to crystallise in flat sheets, and, because there is a perfect cleavage parallel to the sheet, thin flakes of the mineral can easily be peeled away from the surface. These flakes are characteristically flexible and elastic, so that they can be bent and, after bending, they spring back to their original shape.

Muscovite is a major constituent of granites, diorites, slates, mica-schists and gneisses. It is very resistant to chemical weathering, so that flakes eroded from outcrops of igneous and metamorphic rocks are frequently washed or blown into sedimentary environments where they settle and are preserved. The bedding planes on sandstones are often coated with flakes of muscovite deposited in this way. The flakes make it easy to split the rock into slabs along the bedding planes.

Flakes of muscovite are colourless and transparent with a bright, glassy lustre. Thicker crystals are pale brownish-grey in colour with a pearly lustre, and are often spotted with impurities. The hardness is 2·5 and thus it can easily be scratched by a knife, but only with difficulty by your fingernail. When scratched by a knife a characteristic harsh, grating sound is produced.

The flaky habit and good cleavage of muscovite help to distinguish it from other common white or colourless minerals. Some forms of gypsum resemble muscovite at first glance, but gypsum is softer and its flakes are not elastic.

BIOTITE MICA

Biotite, like muscovite, is a silicate of aluminium, potassium and hydrogen, but also contains iron and magnesium. It has the same flaky habit as muscovite but the cleavage is not quite as perfect, so that large, thin flakes are more difficult to detach. It occurs abundantly in many metamorphic and acid igneous rocks but, as it is not nearly as stable chemically as muscovite, it is much less common in sedimentary rocks.

Biotite is usually dark brown to black in colour, shiny and opaque and with an almost metallic bronze lustre. Weathered flakes which have been partially oxidised have a golden-yellow appearance which can be misleading to prospectors. The hardness of biotite is about 3 and it can easily be scratched with a knife.

Biotite can be distinguished from the other common dark-coloured minerals by its flaky habit, good cleavage, and relative softness.

HORNBLENDE

This, the common member of the amphibole family of minerals, is a complex silicate of aluminium, calcium, iron, sodium, magnesium and hydroxyl. It occurs abundantly in many igneous and metamorphic rocks.

Hornblende is a very dark, opaque mineral with a bright, glassy lustre. Its colour varies from a very deep brown or green to black. The hardness is about 5·5 and the mineral can be scratched by a knife only with difficulty.

Well-developed crystals occur in the form of elongated, six-sided prisms. Cross-sections of these are easily recognisable (Fig. 3.3). Hornblende also has two good cleavages parallel to the larger faces of the prism and making an angle of about 56° with one another. Broken fragments of large crystals tend therefore to have the characteristic shape of the parallelogram.

In fine-grained rocks, such as andesite and basalt, the hornblende crystals are usually much too small and too irregular in shape to allow positive identification in the field. Augite, which has a similar colour and hardness and is also common in such rocks, may easily be mistaken for hornblende. The simplest means of identification in these circumstances is by microscopic examination.

AUGITE

Augite, the common member of the pyroxene group of minerals, is a complex silicate of aluminium, calcium, iron and magnesium. It is a major constituent of many igneous rocks, particularly those of basic and ultrabasic composition.

Augite is deep green to black in colour and is opaque with a glassy lustre. The hardness is 5·5 to 6, making the mineral scratchable with a knife only with difficulty.

The crystals tend to be well-formed and, if large enough to be seen, appear as rather stumpy, eight-sided prisms. They also have two cleavages which are almost at right angles to one another. The octagonal cross-section of the prisms and the square-ended cleavage fragments help to distinguish augite from hornblende (Fig. 3.3).

Field identification of augite is difficult in the fine-grained igneous rocks because the crystals are usually too small to show any of the distinctive features. The rectangular cleavage pattern may, however, be visible under a strong lens.

OLIVINE

Olivine, a silicate of magnesium and iron, occurs very commonly in basic and ultrabasic igneous rocks. It is also found in some marbles which have been formed by the contact metamorphism of dolomitic limestones.

The colour of olivine varies from pale to dark yellowish-green, the more iron-rich varieties being almost black in colour. When fresh the crystals are transparent, but normally, owing to the chemical instability of olivine, some alteration will have taken place and the transparency considerably reduced. Olivine has a glassy and slightly oily lustre, so that the crystals tend to have a wet appearance, especially when, as commonly happens in basalt, they are embedded in a dull, fine-grained groundmass. The hardness of olivine is about 6·5, too hard to be scratched by steel.

Well-formed crystals with sharply defined faces are rare, and rather rounded, stumpy, oval-shaped crystals the general rule. Olivine has no cleavage and breaks with a distinctly conchoidal fracture resembling that of quartz. It is distinguished from quartz by its colour, and from augite and hornblende by its superior hardness and lack of cleavage.

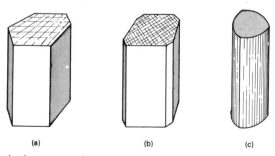

(a)   (b)   (c)

Figure 3.3   Typical cross-sections of crystals: (a) hornblende, showing the six-sided prism with the oblique cleavage; (b) augite, showing the eight-sided prism with almost rectangular cleavage; (c) tourmaline, showing the triangular prism with curved, vertically striated faces.

CHLORITE

The dull, greenish-grey colour of many rocks exposed in the field is due to the presence of minerals of the chlorite group. They are hydrated silicates of aluminium, iron and magnesium, and are produced by the decomposition of iron-rich silicates like olivine, augite, hornblende and biotite. They are therefore very common in weathered igneous rocks and in shales and greywacke sandstones derived from such rocks. Chlorite is also common in low-grade metamorphic rocks like slate and phyllite.

Although chlorite is such an extremely abundant mineral, it is frequently overlooked in the field. This is because large crystals are rarely found. It normally occurs in the form of very small, powdery flakes. Under a strong lens the flakes can be seen to resemble those of mica, but, unlike mica, the flakes of chlorite are not elastic and, when bent, they stay bent. The hardness of chlorite is about 2, and it can be scratched by your fingernail.

The softness of chlorite and its pale greenish-grey colour help to distinguish it from the much harder and more strongly coloured green minerals, malachite and epidote.

EPIDOTE

Epidote is a silicate of aluminium, iron, calcium and hydroxyl. It has a characteristic strong yellowish-green colour and is produced by the decomposition of rocks containing calcium-rich feldspars and iron-rich silicates (i.e. the basic igneous rocks). It is also commonly found in the contact zones of granite intrusions where the green epidote contrasts vividly with the red feldspar and the white quartz to produce a very colourful rock.

Epidote usually occurs as small, irregular grains and shapeless patches impregnating the parent rock. It is rare to find crystals large enough to display any visible structures, but, if found, they are in the form of elongated prisms with one good cleavage. It is a hard mineral, reaching 7 on Mohs' scale.

Epidote is normally identified in the field by its intense and distinctive yellow-green colour. It could be mistaken for chlorite, but a useful field guide in this respect is that, whereas chloritisation very considerably softens the parent rock, epidotisation commonly hardens it. As a consequence chloritised patches on surfaces of rocks undergoing erosion tend to be hollowed out, but in the epidotised areas the reverse is the case with the epidote standing out as raised, knobbly lumps. Epidote might also be mistaken for malachite but the green colour of malachite lacks the yellow tinge of epidote. Malachite is also a much softer mineral.

CALCITE

Calcite is the common form of calcium carbonate and, as the bulk component of limestones and marbles and the cementing agent in many sandstones and mudstones, it is an enormously abundant mineral in the earth's crust. By the evaporation of lime-bearing solutions calcite is precipitated as stalactites and stalagmites in caves and as calcareous tufa in springs and river beds. It is also a very abundant mineral in veins either by itself or mixed with other vein minerals like quartz, fluorite and metal ores.

The crystal habit of calcite is exceedingly variable. In the groundmass of limestones, where calcite is usually mixed with some clay or sand, its habit is compact and massive or, in the case of chalk, powdery. In fossil shells and crinoid stems in the limestone it may, however, be quite coarsely crystalline. In stalactites and stalagmites the habit is normally either fibrous or prismatic, and in veins it is either massive or crystalline with the size of the crystals varying from small, less than 1 cm across, to very large, more than 30 cm across.

Well-developed crystals of calcite are generally either tall and sharply pointed, and hence known as dog-tooth spar, or short and bluntly pointed, and hence known as nail-head spar (Fig. 3.4). Calcite is normally white and translucent to opaque with a glassy lustre. Traces of impurities impart pale shades of yellow, grey, pink or purple to some specimens. Exceptionally pure crystals of calcite are colourless and transparent.

Calcite has three very good cleavages which make angles of about 75° to 80° with one another. As the crystals are brittle they can easily be broken to form cleavage fragments whose rhombic shape is very distinctive. With a hardness of 3 calcite is easily scratched by a knife but not by your fingernail.

The good cleavage easily distinguishes calcite from quartz, and the hardness distinguishes it from gypsum and the feldspars.

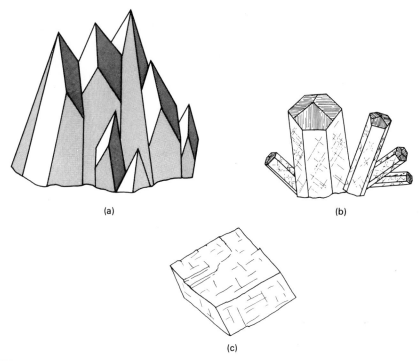

(a)

(b)

(c)

Figure 3.4   Crystals of calcite and dolomite: (a) calcite showing the dog-tooth spar habit; (b) calcite showing the nail-head spar habit; (c) dolomite showing the rhombohedral habit, which is also the cleavage form of calcite.

DOLOMITE

Dolomite, a carbonate of calcium and magnesium, is a common associate of calcite in magnesium-bearing limestones and marbles, and in mineral veins. When pure it is colourless or white with a slightly pearly lustre. Commonly it is tinged a yellowish-brown colour by impurities.

The numerous cavities in dolomitic limestones are frequently lined with crystals of dolomite. The common crystal form is the rhombohedron, and very often the faces of the crystals are **slightly** curved. There are three good cleavages parallel to the crystal faces. The hardness is about 4.

Dolomite resembles calcite but can be distinguished from it by its pearly lustre and by the fact that the simple rhombohedron is a far more common form of crystal growth in dolomite than in calcite (Fig. 3.4).

GARNET

The garnet group of minerals are aluminium silicates containing varying proportions of iron, magnesium and calcium with traces of other metals. They occur abundantly in many metamorphic rocks, especially as crystals up to about 1 cm across in mica-schists and amphibolites. They are also found, sometimes as very large crystals, in limestones and volcanic rocks altered by the heat of nearby intrusions.

All garnets crystallise in complex forms of the cubic system. The rhombic dodecahedron, with twelve diamond-shaped faces, and the icositetrahedron, with twenty-four quadrilateral faces, are the commonest forms. The cubic symmetry and the large number of faces combine to give small crystals an approximately spherical shape. The crystals display no cleavage, but break with an irregularly conchoidal fracture.

The colour of garnet varies from almost black and opaque in the iron-rich variety to deep red and transparent in the magnesium-rich variety. The calcium-rich garnet is light brown and opaque. Garnet is a hard mineral, about 7 on Mohs' scale, and with a specific gravity of about 4 it is relatively quite heavy.

The crystal shape, colour and hardness are the best field guides to the identification of garnet. In mica-schists small, hard garnets protrude from weathered and eroded surfaces rather like raisins on the top of a cake.

TOURMALINE

Tourmaline, a very complex silicate of boron, hydrogen, sodium, aluminium and iron, is particularly common in the granites of Cornwall and Devon and their associated pegmatites and mineral veins. Sometimes, as at Roche, near Bodmin, it may form the bulk of the rock along with quartz.

Tourmaline usually occurs as black, shiny, elongated prisms which at first sight might be mistaken for either hornblende or augite, but on closer inspection reveal several distinctive features. Cross-sections of the prisms are triangular and often slightly curved (Fig. 3.3). The crystal faces are finely striated in the direction of elongation of the prisms.

Tourmaline is a hard mineral, about 7 on Mohs' scale, and this, along with the absence of cleavage also helps to distinguish it from hornblende and augite.

PYRITE

Pyrite, which is a sulphide of iron, is an extremely common accessory mineral in many igneous, metamorphic and sedimentary rocks. It is also very common in mineral veins, where it crystallises in various forms of the cubic system, principally the simple cube, the pentagonal dodecahedron and complex interpenetrant twins of these two forms. One very characteristic feature of the simple cube form is that the faces are striated and the striae on any one face are perpendicular to the striae on the adjacent faces (Fig. 3.5).

Pyrite is a brassy-yellow, opaque mineral with a bright, metallic lustre. On exposure to the atmosphere oxidation takes place and the surface tarnishes to become dull and rusty. With a hardness of 6·5 pyrite cannot be scratched by a knife, and its specific gravity of 5 makes it feel heavy. When hit with a hammer it frequently gives off sparks.

In spite of its popular name of 'fool's gold', pyrite is unlikely to be confused with any other mineral. Its crystal form, colour and hardness are sufficiently distinctive.

CHALCOPYRITE

Chalcopyrite, otherwise known as copper pyrite, is the most widely distributed ore of copper. It occurs in veins along with quartz, calcite and other metal ores. It is also found disseminated in small patches throughout some igneous intrusions.

The habit of chalcopyrite is usually massive, but sometimes crystals of a pyramidal shape occur. The colour is golden yellow often concealed by a tarnish which is orange to black when thick and is in brilliantly iridescent colours when

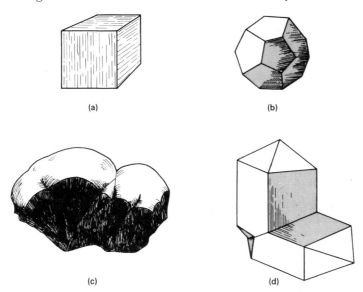

(a)   (b)

(c)   (d)

Figure 3.5   Pyrite, hematite and cassiterite: (a) a typical cube of pyrite showing the striated faces; (b) pyrite in the pentagonal dodecahedron form; (c) hematite in the 'kidney iron ore' variety showing the smooth, rounded exterior and the fibrous internal structure; (d) cassiterite showing the typical knee-shaped twin crystal habit.

thin. Like pyrite it displays no cleavage, but its hardness of 3·5 is much lower than that of pyrite, and it is easily scratched with a knife.

MALACHITE

Copper ores exposed to the oxidising and carbonating effects of the atmosphere commonly break down to form the green copper carbonate, malachite. It is found as grains and encrusting growths coating the sides of veins and the surfaces of other copper ores. The habit is either powdery or compact and massive.

The combination of a pure, bright green colour and a dull, opaque lustre is very distinctive. The hardness of malachite is 4, and this, along with the purer colour, distinguish it from the much softer chlorite and the much harder epidote.

AZURITE

Azurite is a carbonate of copper frequently occurring in association with malachite in the oxidised zones of copper-bearing deposits. It has a very distinctive sky blue colour which is in a pale shade in opaque, powdery specimens and in a deep shade in more massive and translucent crystalline specimens. It is a soft mineral with a hardness of about 4.

Specimens of vein-rocks from the waste tips of abandoned copper mines in Cornwall and North Wales often carry stains, streaks and small patches of azurite and malachite easily spotted by their bright colours.

HEMATITE

Hematite is a dark, heavy oxide of iron which frequently occurs in veins along with quartz, barite and other minerals. Sometimes, as in Cumbria, it is found in very large quantities in pockets in limestone formations. When pure, it contains nearly 70% iron and is a valuable ore.

The crystal habit and colour of hematite is very variable. Impure earthy varieties have a dull purple-red colour but the more compact variety known as 'kidney ore' is steel grey in colour and grows in a radiating, fibrous manner to form nodules with rounded, shiny surfaces (Fig. 3.5). Another variety, specular iron ore, occurs as small, dark crystals with a brilliant metallic lustre. When crushed with a hammer all the varieties give a powder with a characteristic blood-red colour.

The hardness of the compact, crystalline varieties is 6 and the specific gravity about 5. The earthy variety is much softer and not nearly so heavy. The red colour of the powdered mineral distinguishes hematite from all the other common dark-coloured minerals.

MAGNETITE

Magnetite, also known as lodestone, is an oxide of iron. In the form of small black granules it is a common minor constituent of basic and ultrabasic igneous rocks. It is also found in a more massive form in mineral veins and in the contact zones of some intrusions, e.g. Kilchrist in Skye.

Magnetite is dark grey or black in colour and is opaque with a dull metallic lustre. The powder, unlike that of hematite, is black. The hardness of magnetite is 6 and its specific gravity is 5. By far the most distinctive feature of magnetite is the strong magnetic effect (the word 'magnet' is derived from the name of the mineral). When a vein of magnetite is hammered in the field particles of dust and small fragments of the mineral are immediately attracted back to the vein and form a crust on it in exactly the same way as iron filings will encrust a magnet. Newly detached hand specimens of the mineral are often polar and will readily deflect the needle of a compass. No other common black mineral will do this.

LIMONITE

The familiar rusty-brown colour of weathered surfaces of iron-rich igneous, metamorphic and sedimentary rocks is due to a superficial film of the hydroxide of iron, limonite. The mineral also occurs as concretions and nodules in mineral veins and highly weathered rocks. The colour varies from yellowish-brown in soft, powdery specimens to a dark orange-brown in the more solid, concretionary type. The habit of limonite is massive and its hardness varies from 1 to 5 depending on the degree of compactness of the specimen.

The colour and habit of limonite are the features which distinguish it from the other common minerals.

CASSITERITE

Cassiterite is the common ore of tin. It is an oxide and occurs along with quartz, tourmaline and other minerals in veins associated with granite intrusions, especially those of south-west England. It occurs as crystals, usually in the form of stumpy tetragonal prisms capped by tetragonal pyramids. Knee-shaped twins formed by two prisms growing outwards from one another at right angles are a distinctive feature (Fig. 3.5).

The colour of cassiterite is dark brown to black and the crystals have a very bright, almost metallic lustre. It is a hard mineral, about 6·5 on Mohs' scale, and with a specific gravity of 7 it is also very heavy.

Cassiterite is distinguished from the more lustrous varieties of hematite by its crystal form and from the darker varieties of sphalerite by its brighter lustre, superior hardness and greater density.

GALENA

The common ore of lead is the sulphide, galena. It occurs frequently in veins along with sphalerite, calcite, fluorite and quartz. On freshly exposed surfaces the mineral is easily recognisable by its clear silvery-grey colour and mirror-like metallic lustre. On weathered surfaces galena is much less conspicuous as a tarnish causes the colour to fade to a lead-grey and the lustre to become dull.

Galena crystallises in the cubic system, but most commonly its habit is massive. It is a brittle mineral and cleaves easily into small cubes. Its hardness is only 2·5 and it leaves a grey mark when drawn across a sheet of paper. It is very heavy, having a specific gravity of 7·5.

The distinctive colour of galena, combined with its metallic lustre, cubic cleavage, softness and density, make recognition very easy.

SPHALERITE

Sphalerite, also known as blende, is the common ore of zinc. Chemically it is zinc sulphide. It is found in veins along with galena, calcite, fluorite and quartz. It occurs either as small well-shaped crystals in various complex forms of the cubic system or, more commonly, as massive irregular and coarsely crystalline patches within the vein. As sphalerite can be cleaved readily in no less than six different directions cleavage faces are numerous on broken specimens.

The colour of sphalerite can be yellow, orange or red and transparent in small crystals, but more usually it is very dark brown and opaque. The lustre varies from bright and glassy in the transparent varieties to dull and resinous in the opaque variety. With a hardness of about 4 it is easily scratched by a knife. The specific gravity is also 4.

Sphalerite is distinguished from cassiterite by the much greater hardness and density of the latter. The small red crystals of sphalerite found at some localities in Clwyd look like garnets but are, again, much softer.

FLUORITE

Fluorite, or fluorspar, is a simple compound of calcium and fluorine. It is very common in veins in limestone areas, where it occurs along with quartz, calcite, barite and metal ores. It also occurs in altered rocks in the vicinity of granite intrusions. Its habit is crystalline, commonly occurring as cubes in the form of interpenetrant twins (Fig. 3.6). The cleavage is octahedral and cuts obliquely across the corners of the cube to give triangular cleavage faces.

Figure 3.6   Crystals of fluorite from Matlock, Derbyshire showing the characteristic cubic form and interpenetrant twinning.

The colour of fluorite varies all the way from colourless and transparent to very deep purple and opaque. Usually it is found in pale, translucent shades of white, yellow, green and purple. Specimens with bands of white and purple can be found in north Derbyshire, where it is known as 'Blue John', and also in parts of North Wales and the Yorkshire Dales. Fluorite has a hardness of 4 and can easily be scratched by a knife.

The cubic crystals and octahedral cleavage distinguish fluorite from quartz and calcite. Quartz is also very much harder.

GYPSUM

Gypsum is hydrated calcium sulphate. It is found in many sedimentary rocks, chiefly clays and marls. In red beds of desert origin, such as the Triassic rocks in Britain, it may occur as thick seams forming part of the bedded formation. In fossiliferous clays, such as the Gault Clay, gypsum occurs in veins and isolated pockets of crystals. These may be the product of a reaction between iron sulphide, as pyrite, and calcium carbonate, as calcite, in the clay.

The crystal habit of gypsum is very variable. In bedded seams it is commonly fine-grained and massive, white and translucent, mottled with reddish-brown streaks. Under the name of alabaster it is used as a decorative stone.

In veins the habit of gypsum is usually fibrous. The crystals may be colourless and transparent, but more usually they are white and translucent, stained in patches in shades of yellow, brown and red by traces of iron oxides. A very finely fibrous variety with a very distinctive silky lustre is known as satin spar.

Clear, transparent crystals of gypsum are known as selenite. They are tabular in shape and when viewed from the side have the profile of a parallelogram. Frequently the crystals are twinned. When large the crystals may display a pearly lustre, but small crystals are usually glassy.

Crystals of gypsum cleave readily in a direction parallel to the face labelled P in Figure 3.7. The cleavage flakes are flexible, and so could be mistaken for those of muscovite. Unlike muscovite flakes, however, they are not elastic and do not spring back when the pressure is released. Crystals break along the line marked Q–R in the diagram with a distinct crackling sound.

The hardness of gypsum is normally 2 but in the massive variety it may rise to 2·5. It can, therefore, be scratched by your fingernail, but possibly only with difficulty. The low hardness, cleavage and crystal form serve to distinguish gypsum from the other common minerals of light colour.

BARITE

Barite is barium sulphate. It is a common vein mineral and often occurs along with calcite, fluorite, quartz and hematite, as in the Pennine ore-fields. It also forms the cementing agent in some sandstones, notably the Triassic sandstone of the Cheshire–Shropshire basin.

Well-formed crystals of barite are tabular in shape with two large faces forming the base and top of the crystal and numerous small faces around the sides (Fig. 3.7). Barite has good cleavage in three directions.

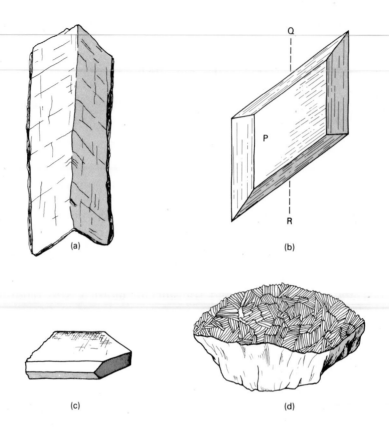

Figure 3.7   Gypsum and barite: (a) gypsum crystal showing arrowhead twinning; (b) simple crystal of gypsum with the principal cleavage running parallel to face P and a secondary cleavage parallel to the plane Q–R along which the crystal can be broken with a distinct snapping sound; (c) part of a tabular crystal of barite; (d) the 'cock's comb spar' variety of barite.

When pure, barite is colourless and transparent with a glassy lustre but commonly the mineral is white and opaque or stained by impurities to give shades of yellow, brown, green or red. The hardness of barite is 3 and its specific gravity is 4·5.

A variety of barite, commonly found lining cavities in veins, consists of numerous platy crystals thickly clustered together in fan-shaped groups more or less parallel to one another. This arrangement gives a very distinctive appearance to the external surface of the specimen and so the variety is known as 'cock's comb spar'. Barite also occurs as aggregates of lamellar, radiating crystals. A very fine-grained stalactitic variety is also known.

The most distinctive property of barite is its weight. Its high density makes it about twice as heavy as most other light-coloured minerals including all the commonly occurring species.

Table 3.3 *Key for the identification of minerals*

Hardness	Lustre	Colour of mineral	Colour when powdered	Cleavages	Specific gravity	Crystal form and habit	Mineral
2 to 2·5	dull or glassy or pearly	colourless or white, but often stained grey, yellow, red or brown	white	one very good forming flakes which are flexible but not elastic	2·3	may be crystalline or massive or fibrous; good crystals are frequently twinned	Gypsum
2 to 2·5	dull or glassy or pearly	light grey-green to dark green	white or pale green	one very good forming flakes which are flexible but not elastic	2·5 to 3	usually occurs as very small powdery flakes and scales	Chlorite
2 to 2·5	glassy or pearly	colourless but may be stained yellow, brown or silvery	white	one very good forming flakes which are flexible and elastic	2·8	fine to coarsely crystalline; readily split into very thin cleavage flakes	Muscovite
2·5 to 3	pearly or weakly metallic	dark grey, dark green, dark brown, or black	white	one very good forming flakes which are flexible and elastic	3	fine to coarsely crystalline; cleavage flakes tend to be small and irregular	Biotite
2·5 to 3	metallic but dull when tarnished	grey	dark grey or black	three at 90° to each other forming cubes	7·5	may occur as large, coarse crystals or as a fine, granular powder	Galena
3	glassy	colourless or white, often stained grey, yellow, pink or purple	white	three very good forming rhombohedral fragments	2·7	good crystals are common, but may also be found in massive and fibrous forms	Calcite

Table 3.3—*continued*

Hardness	Lustre	Colour of mineral	Colour when powdered	Cleavages	Specific gravity	Crystal form and habit	Mineral
3 to 3·5	glassy	colourless or white, often stained brown, yellow, red, or green	white	three good forming rhombic tablets	4·5	fine to coarsely crystalline in radiating and tabular form; also occurs in massive and stalactitic forms	Barite
3·5 to 4	glassy or pearly	colourless or white, often stained brown, yellow or grey	white	three good forming rhombohedral fragments	2·9	commonly occurs as rhombohedral crystals; also found in a massive form with sugary texture	Dolomite
3·5 to 4	glassy or resinous or weakly metallic	yellow, red, brown or black	pale brown	good in six directions	4	occurs in coarsely crystalline and finely granular forms	Sphalerite
3·5 to 4	dull or silky	bright light green or dark green	bright green	not normally seen	4	usually occurs as encrusting fibrous or earthy masses; sometimes finely crystalline	Malachite
3·5 to 4	glassy or dull	bright sky blue or dark blue	sky blue	not normally seen	3·8	usually found as powdery crusts, sometimes as short, flat, prismatic crystals	Azurite
3·5 to 4	metallic	brass yellow often hidden by a coloured or black tarnish	greenish-black	none	4·2	usually occurs in massive form but sometimes found as tetrahedral crystals	Chalcopyrite
4	glassy	colourless, white, white black, or any colour	colourless, white	four good across the corners of the cubes	3·2	good crystals common; sometimes very large; often show twinned cubes on external surfaces	Fluorite

Hardness	Luster	Colour	Streak	Cleavage	Specific gravity	Occurrence / Form	Mineral
5 (down to 1 in earthy varieties)	usually dull but may be weakly metallic	rusty yellow-brown to black	yellow-brown	none	about 4	occurs as earthy or fibrous encrustations on oxidised surfaces	Limonite
5·5 to 6	glassy	dark green, brown or black	light grey-green	two at 56° to one another	3·2	usually occurs in massive or fibrous forms; good crystals rarely seen	Hornblende
5·5 to 6	glassy or dull	dark green, brown or black	light grey-green	two at 87° to one another	3·4	usually occurs in massive form but good crystals showing octagonal cross-sections are fairly common	Augite
5·5 to 6·5	dull or weakly metallic	black	dark grey or black	not well developed	5	usually finely crystalline and massive; octahedral crystals sometimes seen; strongly magnetic	Magnetite
6	glassy	colourless, white often stained pink, brown or yellow	white	two at 90° to one another	2·5	good crystals common, often showing simple twinning	Orthoclase
6 to 6·5	glassy	colourless, white often stained red, brown or yellow	white	two at about 86° to one another	2·6	good crystals not common but when found they show multiple twinning	Plagioclase
5·5 to 6·5	dull or metallic	dark purple-red, grey or black	blood red	not normally seen	5 (lower in earthy varieties)	usually occurs as compact, fibrous or loose, earthy masses; sometimes found as bright, flaky crystals	Hematite
6 to 6·5	metallic	golden yellow often with a rusty tarnish	black	none	5	good crystals common in the form of striated cubes or pentagonal dodecahedra	Pyrite
6·5 to 7	glassy or almost metallic	usually deep brown or black but may be pale brown	pale yellow-brown	poorly developed	7	crystals in the form of tetragonal prisms with knee-shaped twins	Cassiterite

Table 3.3—*continued*

Hardness	Lustre	Colour of mineral	Colour when powdered	Cleavages	Specific gravity	Crystal form and habit	Mineral
6·5 to 7	glassy	pale yellow-green to deep olive-green	white	none	3·3	usually occurs in granular masses; good crystals rare	Olivine
6·5 to 7	glassy	strong, deep yellowish green ('pistachio green')	grey	one good, but not often seen	3·4	commonly occurs as small, irregular grains and patches; sometimes found as crystals	Epidote
7	glassy when crystalline, dull when compact	colourless, white, black and all colours	white	none	2·65	crystals are hexagonal prisms capped by pyramids; prism faces horizontally striated; vein quartz commonly massive; compact varieties are microcrystalline	Quartz
6 to 7·5	glassy	usually dark brown-red, but can be pale brown, green, clear red or black	white	none	4	good crystals are common in forms of rhombic dodecahedra and icositetrahedra; also occurs in massive form	Garnet
7 to 7·5	glassy	usually black but can be colourless, brown, blue, red or green	white	none	3	crystals form radiating, vertically striated needles; needles are triangular in cross-section with curved faces	Tourmaline

4

The Study of Fossils in the Field

INTRODUCTION

LOOKING for, and finding, fossils are two of the most pleasurable aspects of geological fieldwork. Long before geology became a science, and before the origin and significance of fossils were fully understood, people were collecting fossils simply because they were interesting, unusual and rather mysterious objects.

Fossils are the remains and traces of plants and animals preserved in the rocks. When an animal or a plant dies and becomes buried in sediment it usually decays completely leaving no trace of its previous existence. Sometimes, however, the harder or more chemically resistant parts of the organism are preserved long enough to leave an imprint on the surrounding sediment and in some instances, notably with fossil sea shells, the hard parts may be preserved virtually unchanged from their original state.

Animals which crawl over or burrow into soft mud and sand frequently leave tracks and patches of disturbed sediment which survive when the sediment becomes converted to rock and thus, although the animals themselves are not found, their former presence in the sediment is inferred from the occurrence of these trace fossils.

It follows from the mode of origin of fossils that the rocks most likely to contain them are sedimentary rocks deposited in environments favourable to an abundance of plant and animal life. Muds and sands which accumulated on the bottoms of lakes and rivers and in the shallower parts of the sea are obvious examples of potentially rich fossil-bearing deposits. Sediments of desert origin are less likely to contain many fossil remains. Metamorphic and igneous rocks rarely contain fossils, but even here there are exceptions. Distorted, but nevertheless recognisable, trilobites can be found in the slates of North Wales for example, and trees which grew on the flanks of the Carboniferous volcanoes in central Scotland are preserved in the layers of volcanic ash in which they were buried.

Another factor which influences the fossil-bearing capacity of rocks is the age of the rocks. In early Precambrian times, 3000 million years ago, when the world was young, life was apparently restricted to a few primitive algae and bacteria, so that fossils in rocks of this age are hard to come by. It was not until about 600 million years ago that life in the sea was anything like as varied, abundant and preservable as it is at present, and it was only about 300 million years ago that land-based plants and animals began to flourish.

WHERE TO LOOK FOR FOSSILS

We have seen that, as a general rule, the rocks most likely to contain numerous well-preserved fossils are relatively young sedimentary rocks deposited in shallow-water environments. Fine-grained rocks like *clays*, *shales*, *marls* and

Figure 4.1 A limestone, composed of fragments of crinoid stems and ossicles, from the Lower Carboniferous rocks of Clitheroe, Lancashire. Scale: $\frac{1}{3}$ original size.

muddy limestones are particularly favourable. The Silurian Wenlock Limestone of the West Midlands, for example, is so rich in fossils that they constitute the bulk of the rock. The crinoidal limestones so common in the Lower Carboniferous succession in Britain are similar in this respect (Fig. 4.1). In the field it is particularly rewarding to examine the weathered surfaces of such rocks. The fine matrix in which the fossils are embedded tends to be eroded away quite quickly leaving the fossils to stand out in relief, giving the observer a dramatic view of what the sea floor was like at the time of deposition.

Not all the fine-grained sedimentary rocks are fossiliferous. Most of the beds of shale and mudstone forming such a large part of the Upper Carboniferous Coal Measures in Britain are depressingly barren of any signs of former life, and the fossils tend to be restricted to comparatively thin bands within the succession. It is often the case that when fossils do occur in a bed of sedimentary rock they are extremely abundant, but beds immediately above and below the fossil-bearing bed, and similar to it in appearance, contain no visible remains. Why this should be so is not known.

Sandstones in general are less likely to contain fossils than clays and shales. Partly this is because sand is the product of a more turbulent environment and thus, before burial, the organic remains are often broken and abraded by wave and current action. In addition sandstones are much more permeable to water than are rocks of finer grain-size and, consequently, any fossil shells embedded in the sandstones may well be dissolved away by the groundwater in the course of time. Sometimes, however, an imprint of the shell may be left on the rock.

Thinly-bedded, fine-grained sandstones, often found alternating with shales, are particularly good for trace fossils (Fig. 4.2). In coarse-grained sandstones fossils are rare, but occasionally plant remains can be found. Bones and teeth of the larger animals sometimes turn up in coarse sandstones, or even in conglomerates, but usually they are in a rolled and waterworn condition which makes identification difficult.

Fossiliferous **slates** present problems. Not only are the fossils usually quite badly distorted but, as it is only very rarely that the cleavage planes in slates coincide with the bedding planes, the rock tends to split obliquely across the fossils, making them more difficult to find. Graptolites, for example, which are very thin fossils and almost always lie flat along the bedding planes of a shale, are very easily overlooked when a slaty cleavage becomes the dominant feature of the rock.

The best-preserved fossils are usually to be found in **limestones**, but, if the rock is well cemented, extracting the fossils may prove a difficult operation involving protracted chiselling. Fossil collecting is often much more productive from boulders weakened by prolonged weathering than from freshly exposed limestone in quarries and cliffs.

TYPES OF FOSSILS AND THEIR DISTRIBUTION

For a detailed description of the various fossil groups reference should be made to *Fossils* (Introducing Geology series: 1) by Dr F. A. Middlemiss. The two factors which most strongly influence the distribution of fossils and determine which fossils are likely to be found in which rocks are (a) the age of the rocks containing the fossils, and (b) the environment in which these rocks were deposited. By studying the distribution of fossils in the field the pioneer geologists of two hundred years ago established the geological succession of strata and discovered the principles of dating the rocks by means of the contained fossils, even although the actual age in years was at that time still unknown.

The control that the environment in which rocks were deposited had on the kinds of fossils contained in these rocks can best be appreciated by the way in

Figure 4.2   *Pelecypodichnus*, a common trace fossil formed by burrowing lamellibranchs; Upper Carboniferous, Cheesden, Lancashire. Scale: $\frac{1}{3}$ original size.

which the distribution of plants and animals throughout the present-day world is influenced by such factors as climate, distribution of land and sea, mountains, lakes and rivers. Assuming that similar controls operated in the past, it can be deduced from studying all the evidence shown by the fossils and their containing rocks that the trilobites, for example, were marine animals and that some lived in shallow parts of the sea and others were confined to deeper waters.

To the field geologist the most interesting and important groups of fossils in the animal kingdom are the ammonoids, belemnites, brachiopods, corals, crinoids, echinoids, gastropods, graptolites, lamellibranchs and trilobites. In Table 4.1 some of the more important field characteristics of these groups are listed.

Recognising fossils in the field may not be easy. Specimens of the quality displayed in museums or illustrated in textbooks are rarely found. More often than not they are poorly preserved or in fragments or so difficult to extract that they get broken in the process. In spite of this the field geologist is expected to be

Table 4.1 *The field characteristics of the principal fossil groups*

Group	Age range	Rock type in which commonly found	Usual form of preservation
Ammonoids	Devonian to Cretaceous	shale	usually lying flat on bedding planes; often squashed and broken; sometimes only the imprint of the shell remains
		mudstone and muddy limestone	shell usually complete and calcareous; sometimes replaced by pyrite
Belemnites	Carboniferous to Cretaceous (common in Jurassic)	shale, mudstone and limestone	guard usually complete; if numerous specimens are seen on a bedding plane it is worth measuring their alignment to see if there is a preferred orientation
Brachiopods	Cambrian to present (common in Palaeozoic)	limestone and calcareous sandstone	usually complete, the two valves hinged together in the closed position; the shells normally preserved as calcium phosphate or calcium carbonate, but sometimes silicified
Corals	Ordovician to present	limestone (solitary species also found in mudstone and shale)	usually complete and preserved as calcium carbonate, but sometimes silicified
Crinoids	Ordovician to present	limestone	usually disintegrated into individual columnals or short lengths of stem and arms; cup rarely found; columnals usually preserved as coarsely crystalline calcite

Table 4.1—*continued*

Group	Age range	Rock type in which commonly found	Usual form of preservation
Echinoids	Ordovician to present	limestone	the spines nearly always found separated from the test; in Palaeozoic species the test disintegrated into plates; in Mesozoic and Tertiary species the test often complete; usually preserved as calcite, sometimes silicified
Gastropods	Cambrian to present (common in Tertiary and Quaternary)	shale, mudstone and limestone	the shell is usually complete and preserved in the form of calcium carbonate
Graptolites	Cambrian to Carboniferous (common in Ordovician and Silurian)	usually in shale and mudstone, less commonly in limestone	usually found as thin carbonaceous films spread out flat on bedding planes of shales; sometimes pyritised; in limestone may occur in 'solid' (i.e. uncompressed) state
Lamellibranchs	Cambrian to present (common in Tertiary and Quaternary)	shale, mudstone and limestone	the two valves are usually found complete but separate from one another; generally preserved as calcium carbonate, but sometimes pyritised
Trilobites	Cambrian to Permian	shale, mudstone and limestone	often fragmentary; usually preserved as chitin

Figure 4.3   An echinoid preserved in chalk: the spines have become detached from the interambulacral plates which have prominent tubercles; Upper Cretaceous, Lewes, East Sussex. Scale: $\frac{1}{2}$ original size.

43

able in most cases to assign the fossils that he finds to their groups and sometimes to subdivisions within the groups. Consider the crinoids illustrated in Figure 4.1 and the echinoid illustrated in Figure 4.3. In both cases the fossils are incomplete and partially disintegrated. Crinoids normally occur in this state and can be recognised by the variety of oblique and transverse cross-sections of the ossicles and short lengths of stem. The echinoid can be recognised by the distinctive shape of the spines and the interambulacral plates. Identifying to which particular species these fossils belong would not usually be attempted in the field. It would be done later in the laboratory with the aid of reference books.

5
The Identification of Rocks in the Field

INTRODUCTION

THE rocks which constitute the earth's crust consist essentially of assemblages of various minerals. They can be broadly classified, depending upon their mode of origin, into three major divisions, the sedimentary, metamorphic and igneous rocks.

Sedimentary rocks include deposits of sand, mud, sea-shells, salt, peat, etc., which accumulate in favourable localities on the earth's surface. In the course of time these deposits may become consolidated to form sandstone, mudstone, lime-stone, rock-salt, coal, etc., but it should be noted that in the strictly geological sense the loose, unconsolidated deposits, such as sand on the beach, are just as much sedimentary rocks as are their hard, consolidated equivalents (Table 5.1).

Metamorphic rocks originate within the earth's crust and are formed by intense heat or pressure or, more usually, both heat and pressure, acting on the pre-existing rocks so that changes take place in the structure and mineral composition of these rocks, but little or no melting occurs in the process (Table 5.2).

Igneous rocks are formed when hot, molten magma (essentially a solution of rock-forming silicates) cools down and solidifies. This may take place either within the earth's crust to form the intrusive igneous rocks, or on the surface of the earth as volcanic eruptions forming the extrusive igneous rocks (Table 5.3).

The rocks within each of the major divisions are classified partly by the shape and size of the individual particles which make up the rock and partly by which of the rock-forming minerals are present in significant amounts. Gabbro, for instance, is an igneous rock composed of coarse crystals (i.e. measuring more than about 5 mm across) of plagioclase feldspar and augite. It usually contains measurable quantities of other minerals, such as olivine, hornblende and magnetite, but these are not essential constituents of the rock. Conglomerate on the other hand is a sedimentary rock consisting of rounded pebbles embedded in finer-grained matrix. In theory there should be no difficulty in applying the principles of classification to rocks like gabbro and conglomerate. In practice it is sometimes quite difficult to classify and identify a rock in the field, particularly if it is fine-grained.

Consider, for example, basalt, mudstone and hornfels, three very different types of rock. In each case the texture is fine-grained and the colour a dark grey, so that superficially they resemble one another, making identification in the field, without the aid of microscopes and other laboratory equipment, something of a problem. In such cases the **field relationships** of the rocks provide important clues regarding their origin and identity. Among these are the way in which the rock has weathered, whether or not it is part of a stratified sequence, whether it is part of an intrusive body of rock, or whether it is part of some older sequence which has been affected by some nearby intrusion. Field observations of this kind make it possible in many instances to eliminate some of the possibilities and so arrive at a more definite conclusion regarding the identity of the rock.

FIELD CHARACTERISTICS OF SEDIMENTARY ROCKS

For classification purposes the sedimentary rocks are divided into four main categories. These are (a) rocks of **detrital** origin, such as sandstones and conglomerates, composed mainly of fragments which have been eroded from pre-existing rocks, (b) rocks which have been **precipitated** from aqueous solutions, such as some limestones and ironstones, (c) **organic** deposits composed largely of plant and/or animal remains, e.g. coal and many limestones, and (d) **residual** deposits, such as some clays and flint gravels, which are the insoluble residues left on the earth's surface after prolonged chemical weathering. For a more detailed description of the nature and origin of the different types of sedimentary rocks the reader is referred to Chapter 7 of *Rocks and Minerals* (Introducing Geology series: 4).

The coarse-grained detrital rocks are usually quite easy to identify. Rocks composed largely of rounded pebbles or boulders are conglomerates if consolidated and gravels if unconsolidated. Breccias, on the other hand, are composed mainly of angular rock fragments like those in screes. The distinctive features of boulder clay, which in northern parts of Britain is by far the commonest of the sedimentary rocks, are the poor degree of sorting of the clay, sand, pebbles and boulders which compose the rock, and the scratched, smoothed and polished surfaces of many of the pebbles and boulders as a result of glacial erosion.

The medium-grain-sized range of detrital sediments includes the sands and sandstones, and usually these are easily recognisable. The rough, gritty feel of most sandstones is an obvious clue to their detrital origin and when examined with a lens the rocks can be seen to be made up largely of quartz grains. Cross-stratification (Fig. 5.1) and ripple-marking (Fig. 5.2) occur more frequently in sandstones than in any other type of sedimentary rock. Sedimentary quartzites composed of pure quartz sand cemented with silica are difficult to distinguish from metamorphic quartzites and, if in doubt, it is advisable to look closely at any interbedded rocks to see if they provide more positive evidence of a sedimentary or metamorphic origin.

Some of the fine-grained greywacke sandstones which are common in the Ordovician and Silurian rocks of North Wales, the Lake District and southern Scotland are so very similar in appearance to the volcanic rocks from which they have been mainly derived that a very close search for distinctive sedimentary

Figure 5.1   Cross-stratification in Triassic sandstone, Thurstaston, Wirral, Mersey-side.

structures is necessary before they can be positively identified. The most reliable clue in such rocks is usually the bedding. This is frequently graded, becoming coarser, and thus more easily recognisable as detrital in origin, towards the base of each bed (Fig. 5.3).

Fine-grained detrital sedimentary rocks such as clay, mudstone and shale are generally less resistant to erosion than most other rocks. One consequence of this is that ground occupied by such sediments is quite likely to be low-lying and badly drained. Natural outcrops tend therefore to be few, but the widespread use of clay and shale to make bricks and cement means that man-made exposures of these rocks are relatively common. The fresh, unweathered clay and shale found in such exposures frequently provide very well-preserved fossils (Fig. 5.4), and thus it is important when surveying an area to visit any working clay pits and shale quarries if at all possible.

Shale can be split readily into thin sheets running parallel to the bedding planes. It can sometimes be confused with slate which has a similar tendency to split into thin layers. The two can easily be distinguished, however, by means of a simple test. When tapped gently with a hammer shale emits a dull, hollow sound, whereas the much more brittle slate gives out a sharp, clear, ringing note.

Limestones formed by the precipitation of calcium carbonate are mostly of marine origin. Commonly in warm, shallow seas agitated by gentle currents, the grains of sand and small fragments of shells become coated with layers of calcium carbonate. When almost spherical and about 1 mm in diameter these grains are known as ooliths. In former times, especially in the Jurassic Period, thick deposits of ooliths accumulated to form oolitic limestones. The fine, even

Figure 5.2   Ripple-marked sandstone from the Upper Carboniferous at Edenfield, Lancashire; the small, circular depressions are worm burrows.

Figure 5.3   Roadside exposure of sandstone showing graded bedding; Rhayader, Powys.

Figure 5.4   Fragments of trilobites in shale from the Ordovician rocks at Llandrindod Wells, Powys. Scale: $\frac{1}{2}$ original size.

texture of these limestones makes them excellent material for building construction, consequently the distinctive and easily recognisable oolitic structure can be examined in the walls of many churches, cathedrals, office-blocks, banks and town halls as well as in quarries and natural outcrops in the field.

Calcium carbonate is precipitated in the form of stalagmites and stalactites by the slow evaporation of lime-rich groundwater which has percolated through fissures and into cavities in limestone formations. Thick deposits of solid, crystalline limestone are sometimes built up in this way. A somewhat similar process takes place around the margins of springs and in streams where the water is saturated with calcium carbonate. The precipitated lime encrusts the stems and leaves of plants and may eventually clog up the stream with thick layers of the soft, crumbly, porous limestone known as tufa.

Sedimentary ironstones are formed by the precipitation of iron as the carbonate, siderite, or the hydrated oxide, limonite, or the sulphide, pyrite, or the complex silicate, chamosite. In Britain all the more important precipitated ironstones are Jurassic in age. They are low-grade ores, however, and contain significant amounts of detrital sand and fragmented fossils as well as the iron-bearing minerals. Surface exposures of the ironstones are subject to rapid weathering and oxidation. Unweathered specimens are best obtained from working pits and quarries.

By far the most abundant of the organically derived sedimentary rocks are limestones composed of the remains of animals and plants which during their lifetime grew protecting shells or supporting skeletons of calcium carbonate. As a result of this process limestones consisting almost entirely of the fossilised remains of brachiopods (Fig. 5.5), or ammonites (Fig. 5.6), or corals (Fig. 5.7) occur quite frequently. In some cases the fossils are still more or less in the growth positions which they had when the animals were alive, so that delicate structures, such as the spines on a brachiopod valve, are preserved intact. These are known as **life**

Figure 5.5   Limestone composed mainly of brachiopod shells; Lower Carboniferous, Halkyn Mountain, Clwyd. Scale: $\frac{1}{3}$ original size.

assemblages. In other cases the fossil remains have been swept away from the place where they originally grew by currents which deposited them elsewhere, inevitably suffering some wear and tear in the process. These are known as **death assemblages**. By making accurate observations of the attitudes of fossils it is possible to determine whether they form a life or a death assemblage. No expensive equipment is needed, only a keen power of observation. Typical signs of a death assemblage include worn and broken brachiopod shells, overturned compound corals and partially or completely disintegrated graptolites (Fig. 5.8).

The commonest organically derived sedimentary rocks of non-marine origin are peat and coal. Both are the products of prolonged accumulation of dead

Figure 5.6   Limestone containing numerous ammonites; Jurassic, Whitby, North Yorkshire. Scale: $\frac{1}{2}$ original size.

Figure 5.7   Limestone rich in fossil coral; Lower Carboniferous, Settle, North Yorkshire. Scale: $\frac{1}{2}$ original size.

vegetation in badly drained swampy and boggy areas. Exposures of peat are plentiful in upland regions. Natural exposures of coal seams are rare, however, since even quite thin seams have usually been mined at some time or other. Coal obtained from the outcrop is usually stained with rusty-brown patches of limonite due to oxidation of the traces of pyrite commonly present in coal. It also has a marked tendency to crumble into small rectangular fragments. Beds of shale or mudstone lying immediately above a coal seam are well worth a close search for

Figure 5.8   Fragmented graptolites in Ordovician shale from Aber Eiddy Bay near St David's, Dyfed: the graptolites are *Didymograptus*, but the fragments could be mistaken for *Monograptus*; note the preferred orientation of the fossils which is probably due to the action of currents at the time of deposition. Scale: $\frac{1}{2}$ original size.

fossils because it is in just this position that layers crowded with lamellibranchs and, sometimes, ammonoids, are to be found.

Sedimentary rocks of residual origin are not common in Britain, but the flint-bearing clay which occurs lying above the chalk in some areas may well be a deposit of this type. It is thought that slightly acid rainwater slowly dissolves the calcium carbonate of the chalk to leave behind a mixture of fine clay and flint nodules as a practically insoluble residue. These deposits are frequently found capping the flat, plateau-like tops of the hills in chalk country. On the steep flanks of the hills the clay and the flint pebbles tend to be washed down into the main river valleys where they are deposited as alluvial mud and gravel.

If our climate were warmer than it is at present and there were heavy seasonal rainfall, the solution process would continue a stage further. Silica would be slowly leached from the clay so that eventually the residue consists of a mixture of hydrated iron oxide and aluminium oxide. If iron-rich it is known as laterite, if aluminium-rich, bauxite. Laterite and bauxite, though not common in the British succession, occur to a limited extent as reddish-brown, earthy deposits in the Carboniferous and Tertiary sequences and indicate that the climate in those times was very different from now.

Table 5.1   *Key for the identification of sedimentary rocks*

Grain-size and texture	Colour	Occurrence	Distinguishing features	Rock
pebble-sized rock fragments in a finer matrix	matrix usually red or brown; fragments variable	interbedded with other water-deposited sediments	rounded pebbles	**gravel**, if loose; **conglomerate**, if indurated
		interbedded with other sediments usually of non-marine origin	angular fragments	**scree**, if loose; **breccia**, if indurated
boulders and pebbles in a matrix of sandy clay	matrix usually dark shades of grey or brown	interbedded with loose sand and gravel	some boulders angular with flat, striated faces	**boulder clay**
sand-sized particles	brown, red, yellow, grey, green or near white	interbedded with other sediments	feels gritty	**sand**, if loose; **sandstone**, if indurated
	white or near white	interbedded with other indurated sedimentary rocks	smooth, hard and brittle	**sedimentary quartzite**

Table 5.1—*continued*

Grain-size and texture	Colour	Occurrence	Distinguishing features	Rock
very fine particles	dark grey, brown or reddish-brown	interbedded with other sediments	plastic and slippery when wet	**clay**
			compact, without the lamination of shale	**mudstone**
			splits in thin layers along bedding planes	**shale**
fine to coarse particles; sometimes oolitic	usually grey or buff	interbedded with other sediments	may contain many fossils	**limestone**
			crystalline and porous; few fossils	**dolomite**
fine particles	white or near white	interbedded with other sediments	usually powdery and easily broken but sometimes hard and splintery	**chalk**
fine to coarse particles; often oolitic	dark grey or green, weathering to rust brown	interbedded with other sediments	relatively heavy	**ironstone**
coarse, fibrous	brown	interbedded with sand and mud	abundant plant remains	**peat**
very fine, smooth	dark brown or black	interbedded with other indurated sedimentary rocks	shiny, or dull and powdery	**coal**
fine, earthy	reddish-brown	residue from weathering of iron-rich rocks	relatively heavy	**laterite**
	grey or brown	residue from weathering of aluminium-rich rocks	relatively light	**bauxite**

FIELD CHARACTERISTICS OF METAMORPHIC ROCKS

The strong heat and intense pressure to which the rocks in some parts of Britain were subjected during major mountain-building episodes have caused these rocks to display complex folding, faulting and metamorphism. A conspicuous feature of the metamorphism is the frequent development of new minerals, such as garnets and micas.

In Snowdonia and the Lake District, where the regional metamorphism is low in grade, some of the rocks which were originally mudstone, shale or volcanic ash have been metamorphosed to slate. The most distinctive and commercially valuable feature of slate is the well-developed cleavage which enables the rock to be split readily into thin sheets. This cleavage results from the growth, during metamorphism, of minute flakes of mica and chlorite at right angles to the direction of greatest compression.

Exposures in slate quarries are worth a detailed study to see if the relationship between the bedding planes and the cleavage planes can be determined. The cleavage planes tend to lie parallel to the axial planes of the folds and thus cut across the bedding planes at angles which, as measurement with a clinometer will show, vary according to the position in the fold structure at which the readings are taken (Fig. 5.9).

At the crests of the folds the cleavage planes cut the bedding planes at right angles, but on the limbs of the folds the angle between the cleavage and bedding planes is low. Because of the small angle the slate tends to cleave rather poorly on the limbs of the folds and will split along the bedding planes instead. On the crests of the folds, however, the slate cleaves easily along the cleavage planes, and it is from there that the top quality roofing slates are obtained.

A conspicuous feature of some beds of slate are crystals of pyrite showing their characteristic cubic symmetry. Very occasionally squashed and deformed fossils are also found.

As the degree of metamorphism increases, slate grades into phyllite. This is similar in structure to slate, but is more lustrous in appearance due to the enhanced growth of flakes of mica and chlorite along the cleavage planes. Phyllite in turn grades into schist, whose layered structure is the result of close packing of flaky and elongated minerals in a direction all more or less parallel to one another. This schistosity enables such rocks to be split into slabs, but the frequent presence

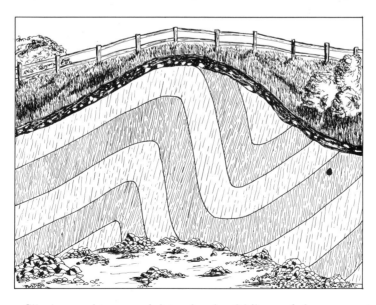

Figure 5.9   Silurian sandstones and slates showing folding and cleavage: note that the cleavage is much more pronounced in the beds of slate than in the beds of sandstone.

of knots of minerals of a non-flaky or non-linear habit, such as garnet, and the increasing complexity of the folding of the rocks combine to make the cleavage in schist not nearly so regular as in slate.

Slate and schist differ so much in appearance that they are unlikely to be confused with one another, but the differences between slate and phyllite on the one hand and phyllite and schist on the other are so small that it is often quite difficult to decide to which group a particular rock belongs. A similar problem arises at the upper end of the scale of metamorphism where there is a gradual transition from schist to gneiss. In comparison with a typical schist, a typical gneiss is a relatively coarse-grained rock, but although the minerals are distributed in bands to give gneiss a foliated appearance not unlike that of schist, the rock cannot be split into slabs along the foliation planes nearly so readily.

A problem arises in the identification of another common metamorphic rock, quartzite. Metamorphic quartzite is a very hard, brittle rock, usually pale in colour and with a smooth, almost flinty texture, but so also is sedimentary quartzite, and unless the field relationships can help it may be difficult to determine whether a particular quartzite is a sedimentary or a metamorphic rock.

Some metamorphic quartzites, such as the Holyhead Quartzite from Anglesey, contain a little mica and chlorite which give the rock a slightly foliated texture. Original sedimentary structures, such as ripple-marks and cross-stratification, can sometimes still be recognised, even if the quartzite has been quite strongly metamorphosed. These structures can be used in the field to determine whether exposed beds are the right way up or not. In a cross-stratified bed which has been overturned during folding the convex curves will face upwards, as you can prove for yourself by turning Figure 5.1 on page 46 upside-down. In a bed which has not been overturned the convex curves of the stratification face downwards. Simple observations of such structures have proved of great value in unravelling the complex folds of metamorphic rock successions.

Marbles, in general, do not differ greatly in outward appearance from the sedimentary limestones from which they have been derived. A close examination with a hand-lens reveals the fine crystals of calcite which give some marbles a distinctive sugary texture. The recrystallisation of the calcite during metamorphism generally destroys all traces of any fossils originally present.

In the field some marbles look not unlike quartzites, but they can easily be distinguished by simply drawing the point of your hammer or chisel across the specimen. A marble can be scratched easily, but no impression is left upon a quartzite.

The most interesting marbles are those derived from the metamorphism of impure limestones. Silica, aluminium, iron, magnesium and calcium combine in a variety of ways to produce a host of new minerals. These include epidote, garnet, olivine, pyroxene and amphibole. Rocks of this type, rich in garnet and pyroxene, are sometimes found at the contacts between impure limestones and igneous intrusions. They are known as skarns, and provide a happy hunting ground for keen mineral collectors.

Table 5.2   *Key for the identification of metamorphic rocks*

Grain-size and texture	Colour	Occurrence	Distinguishing features	Rock
fine or very fine	dark grey, purple or green	in areas of low-grade regional metamorphism	splits readily along well-defined cleavage planes	**slate**
fine	grey-green with silvery sheen	in areas of low- to medium-grade regional metamorphism	splits along cleavage planes; often contorted	**phyllite**
medium to coarse; schistose	dark grey, brown or silvery grey	in areas of medium-grade regional metamorphism	splits parallel to the schistosity; often strongly contorted	**schist**
coarse; banded	mixed white, grey, pink, and black bands	in areas of high-grade regional metamorphism	no tendency to split in any preferred direction; often strongly contorted	**gneiss**
medium; smooth	white or near white	in most metamorphic environments	hard and brittle	**metamorphic quartzite**
fine to coarse; sugary	pale grey or white	in most metamorphic environments	scratched by steel	**marble**

FIELD CHARACTERISTICS OF IGNEOUS ROCKS

Igneous rocks, when examined in the field, can be roughly divided into two main categories. There are those in which the groundmass of the rock is obviously crystalline, and those in which the groundmass is either glassy or composed of crystals too fine-grained to be identifiable even with the aid of a hand-lens.

Into the first category come (a) pegmatites, very coarse-grained rocks in which most of the crystals are over 3 cm in diameter, (b) granites, syenites, diorites, gabbros and peridotites, all of which are coarse-grained rocks (i.e. the majority of the crystals are between about 5 mm and 3 cm in diameter) generally found only in larger intrusions, and (c) microgranites, porphyrites and dolerites, medium-grained rocks (i.e. between 1 mm and 5 mm in average grain size) generally found in sills, dykes and other minor intrusions.

Identification of the crystalline igneous rocks depends partly on their mineral composition and partly on their texture. Rocks of the granite series (i.e. microgranite, granite and granite-pegmatite) are recognised by the crystals of quartz, feldspar and mica which they contain in abundance. In some granites all the crystals are roughly the same size. Others have a porphyritic texture consisting of large, well-formed crystals embedded in a groundmass of much smaller crystals.

A good example of this type is the granite from Shap in Cumbria, which has large crystals of pink orthoclase feldspar in a groundmass of quartz, mica and white plagioclase feldspar. The overall colour of granites, typically pale shades of grey, brown, pink or brick red, largely depends on the colouring of the dominant feldspar in the rock.

Syenites and diorites, because they contain little or no quartz, are easy to distinguish from granites, but they are not so easy to distinguish from one another in the field. The difference between the two lies mainly in the types of feldspar which they contain. In syenites the potassium-rich and sodium-rich feldspars predominate whereas in diorites calcium-rich varieties are found. As a detailed microscopic examination is necessary in order to identify most feldspars precisely, the exact identification of specimens of syenite and diorite in the field is difficult.

Gabbro, composed essentially of plagioclase feldspar and augite, and often also containing olivine, is a dark, heavy, coarse-grained rock. In large gabbro intrusions, such as Carrock Fell in Cumbria and the Cuillin Hills in Skye, there is much variation in grain-size, so that in some parts of the intrusion the rock is fine enough to be more strictly a dolerite than a gabbro, and in other parts it is coarse enough to be the pegmatitic form of gabbro. Gabbro weathers slowly to give a very rough, knobbly surface which is ideal for rock climbing due to the good grip it provides. In this respect it contrasts sharply with granite whose weathered surfaces tend to be rather smooth and very slippery.

Dolerite, containing the same essential minerals as gabbro but in the medium range of grain-size, is a rock commonly found in dykes and sills. Frequently in such intrusions it displays polygonal jointing due to contraction of the rock on cooling. Weathered outcrops of dolerite often have a distinctive spheroidal structure (Fig. 5.10). This is the result of the penetration of the weathering agents, principally air and water, along the joints, so that the rock close to the joints is

Figure 5.10   Spheroidal weathering of a dolerite sill at North Queensferry, Fife.

weakened. As weathering proceeds the blocks gradually assume a more rounded shape, with concentric layers of rusty brown, weathered dolerite wrapped around a central core of fresh dolerite. When completely weathered the blocks disintegrate to form a heavy, brown soil. The entire range from unweathered, through partially weathered, to completely weathered dolerite can often be found in old quarries and roadside cuttings.

Igneous rocks with a very fine-grained or glassy groundmass form when the cooling and solidification of magma takes place so rapidly that there is insufficient time for large crystals to form. This rapid cooling of magma commonly occurs in lava flows extruded from volcanoes and at the margins of intrusions. The common rocks formed in this way are basalts, andesites, trachytes and rhyolites.

Basalt, the fine-grained equivalent of gabbro, is a heavy rock with a dark greenish-grey colour. It may be porphyritic in texture due to a partial crystallisation of the magma before the final rapid stage of cooling, and in such cases the porphyritic crystals of white plagioclase feldspar or dark augite and, possibly olivine, are large enough to be identified with the aid of a hand-lens.

A conspicuous feature of many basalts which have originated from lava flows is an abundance of small cavities giving the rock a bubbly or frothy appearance. This is known as vesicular structure and was formed by bubbles of gas and steam escaping from the lava just before it solidified. Sometimes the vesicles are almost spherical, at other times they are elongated in the direction the lava was flowing. Frequently the vesicles become filled at some later date with secondary minerals such as calcite and chlorite. These infillings are known as amygdales and the rock is said to be amygdaloidal.

Weathering of basalt takes place quite rapidly, so that exposed faces of the rock in abandoned quarries soon become rusty brown in colour as a result of the oxidation of the iron-rich minerals. The weathering proceeds in much the same way as in dolerite. The feldspar ultimately decays to form clay minerals, so that soils derived from weathered basalt and dolerite tend to be heavy clay soils with a rich brown colour.

Andesite, the fine-grained equivalent of diorite, is similar in appearance to basalt, but is a little lighter in colour. Andesite is often porphyritic, with crystals of plagioclase feldspar, biotite, augite and hornblende which, if seen, help to identify the rock. Extensive outcrops of andesite occur in Snowdonia, the Lake District, the Cheviots and central Scotland, often in association with beds of volcanic ash. In the Lake District much of the volcanic ash was later metamorphosed to slate.

Trachyte, the fine-grained equivalent of syenite, generally contains a high proportion of feldspar, and consequently it is usually pale grey, yellow, or pink, but weathers to a darker reddish-brown shade. It is very often porphyritic, sometimes containing quite large crystals of a clear variety of orthoclase known as sanidine and sometimes crystals of sodium-rich plagioclase, biotite, augite and hornblende. The groundmass is usually rough and stony in appearance and distinctly porous.

Trachytes are not as common as basalts and andesites, but they occur extensively in the Devonian and Carboniferous volcanic sequences in central Scotland, particularly in East Lothian where the trachytic volcanic necks of

Figure 5.11   Flow-banded structure in rhyolite from The Wrekin in Salop.

Traprain Law, North Berwick Law and the Bass Rock form conspicuous features of the landscape.

Rhyolite, the fine-grained member of the granite series, is a hard, brittle rock with much the same texture as flint. It is usually light grey or buff in colour but may also be a dark, brick-red shade. Distinctive features of many rhyolites are thin streaks and irregularly contorted bands of alternately lighter and darker colour running through the rocks (Fig. 5.11). This structure, known as flow-banding, is believed to be due to the molten lavas from which the rocks were derived being so sticky and thick that thorough mixing was prevented, so allowing streaks and bands of slightly differing compositions to persist. Good examples of flow-banded rhyolites occur at Caer Caradoc in Salop and at Glen Coe in western Scotland.

Some rhyolites are porphyritic, containing small crystals of clear, glassy quartz and feldspar. Pitchstone, a variety of rhyolite in which the groundmass is almost entirely glassy, occurs in sills and dykes on Arran and Skye. Its dark greenish-grey colour and bright, smooth, resinous surfaces make it an easily recognisable rock.

Rhyolite, a rock which is very resistant to weathering, produces steep-sided, craggy hills and mountains in inland districts and high, rugged cliffs in coastal areas.

Agglomerate and tuff are rocks composed of material which has been ejected from erupting volcanoes in the form of fragmented blocks of all shapes and sizes from huge boulders to fine volcanic ash. Agglomerate, consisting of angular fragments of andesite and basalt embedded in a grey groundmass of fine ash, is one of the commonest rocks occurring in Snowdonia. Similar rocks can be found in most parts of Britain where there have been volcanic eruptions.

Tuff is a finer-grained rock and is simply volcanic ash which has been cemented to form a solid rock. It is usually a light greenish-grey colour and, unlike agglomerate, is often quite well stratified. It could be confused with sandstone or mudstone, but examination with a hand-lens usually reveals small, broken pieces of igneous rock scattered through the fine, dusty matrix. Tuff occurs interbedded with other volcanic rocks in most areas where volcanoes have been active in the past.

Table 5.3 *Key for the identification of igneous rocks*

Grain-size and texture	Colour	Occurrence	Distinguishing features	Rock
very coarse; crystalline	variable depending on composition	veins and intrusions	large, well-formed crystals	**pegmatite**
coarse; crystalline	light grey, brown or pink	large intrusions	abundant quartz and feldspar	**granite**
	light grey, brown or pink	large intrusions	much feldspar; little or no quartz	**syenite**
	medium grey, speckled	large intrusions	much plagioclase and augite or hornblende	**diorite**
	dark grey, speckled	large intrusions	much plagioclase and augite; sometimes olivine	**gabbro**
medium; crystalline	light grey, brown or pink	veins and minor intrusions	abundant quartz and feldspar	**micro-granite**
	medium grey	dykes and sills associated with andesites	much porphyritic feldspar	**porphyrite**
	dark grey	dykes and sills	spheroidal weathering common	**dolerite**
fine or very fine; crystalline; frequently, but not always, porphyritic	light grey or buff	lava flows and volcanic necks	porphyritic quartz and feldspar; often flow-banded	**rhyolite**
	light grey or buff	lava flows and volcanic necks	porphyritic feldspar; sometimes flow-banded; rough, stony appearance	**trachyte**
	medium to dark grey	lava flows and volcanic necks	porphyritic feldspar, biotite, augite, hornblende	**andesite**
	dark grey	lava flows, volcanic necks, dykes and sills	porphyritic feldspar and augite; sometimes olivine	**basalt**

Grain-size and texture	Colour	Occurrence	Distinguishing features	Rock
glassy	dark greenish grey	dykes and sills	shiny, resinous lustre	**pitchstone**
coarse; pyroclastic	dark or light grey-green	interbedded with lava flows	angular blocks in a fine matrix	**agglomerate**
fine; pyroclastic	dark or light grey-green	interbedded with lava flows	fine, ashy texture; often well stratified	**tuff**

6
Making a Geological Map

INTRODUCTION

WHEN carrying out geological fieldwork the basic procedure consists of:

(a) choosing a suitable area for study;

(b) plotting on a map of the area the exact location of all the rock outcrops studied;

(c) identifying, as accurately as possible, all the rocks, minerals and fossils found at these outcrops;

(d) measuring all the details of the rock succession and structure which can be measured, and keeping an accurate record of these measurements in a field notebook;

(e) constructing a geological map which shows the distribution of the various types of rock throughout the area.

For many purposes, especially if time is limited, only the first four steps need be carried out, but the final step, the construction of the geological map, is the ultimate object in fieldwork. To do this to a really high standard requires several years of professional training and practice, but there is no reason why a beginner in geology should not try to make a simple geological map of an area. The first step, the choice of a suitable area, is often the crucial one if serious field mapping is to be attempted.

CHOICE OF AN AREA

The ideal area in which to begin field mapping would be one where plenty of easily accessible rock exposures are evenly distributed over the area, and these show a variety of contrasted rock types and structures, not too complex to make the task impossible nor too simple to make it boring. It is hardly necessary to add that there are few, if any, places in Britain that completely fill these specifications. There are, however, several which come close to doing so.

In southern England one of the best areas is in south Dorset between Weymouth and Swanage where the folded and faulted shales, sandstones and limestones of Jurassic and Cretaceous age offer splendid opportunities for field mapping. In the Mendip Hills, south of Bristol, the field relationships between an older group of Silurian, Devonian and Carboniferous rocks and a younger group of Triassic and Jurassic rocks offer similar opportunities.

In South Wales magnificent exposures of folded and faulted Devonian and Carboniferous strata can be studied in the Gower Peninsula and the coastal areas around Tenby and Milford Haven. Farther north, around St David's, the landscape superbly illustrates the differing resistances that the igneous and sedimentary rocks of the area offer to weathering and erosion. A similar mixture of rocks of the same Precambrian, Cambrian and Ordovician age produces the fascinating coastline of the Lleyn Peninsula in North Wales. Near-by Anglesey has a range of metamorphic rocks unequalled by any other area of comparable size in Britain.

In the Peak District the Carboniferous shales, sandstones, limestones and basalts produce a wealth of fossils, minerals and contrasting landforms. In the central Pennine area of Ingleborough, Settle and Malham the unconformity between the older, folded rocks and the overlying, nearly horizontal Carboniferous Limestone is traceable for several miles, with the Craven Fault providing an additional complication. In Cumbria one of the best areas for field studies is between Appleby and Cross Fell. Here folded and faulted sedimentary and igneous rocks of Ordovician, Silurian, Carboniferous and New Red Sandstone age provide a wide variety of structures and rock types.

In south-west Scotland the richly fossiliferous limestones and shales of the Girvan area are interspersed with numerous basic and ultrabasic igneous rocks to make it an area of exceptional interest, and in south-east Scotland the coast between Edinburgh and Berwick provides many fine exposures of many different kinds of sedimentary and igneous rocks. Among the many good mapping areas in western Scotland the Isle of Islay is first class for the study of metamorphic rocks. Farther north, the Isle of Skye, especially its southern part, and the adjoining Isle of Raasay are unsurpassed for variety of rock types, abundance of fossils and minerals, and diversity of structure.

Northern Ireland also provides several very good field areas. Around Ballycastle, for instance, there are extensive exposures of sedimentary, igneous and metamorphic rocks. There are also unconformities to trace, and folds and faults to measure.

Many other localities in Britain are just as good as those mentioned above. There are, indeed, few places completely devoid of features of geological interest, even in the centres of large towns and cities.

PLOTTING LOCALITIES ON THE MAP

In detailed geological survey work it is essential that the exact locations of the outcrops being studied are plotted on a base map of the area. If Ordnance Survey maps on the 1 : 10 000 or six inches to one mile scales are being used, there is rarely much difficulty in pinpointing the exact position of an outcrop since these maps provide a very detailed plan of the topography of the area with roads, footpaths, field boundaries, woods, streams and many other landmarks all clearly shown. A little practice in the reading of maps is all that is required.

Sometimes, however, problems arise. It may happen that the outcrops are on a moorland plateau with few obvious landmarks in the immediate vicinity, or they may be in an area where there have been substantial changes to the landscape since the map was printed. New roads may have been constructed or the field boundaries altered so that the exact position of a locality on the map is not clear. In such cases compass bearings are taken on more distant landmarks. These are done with a compass in which bearings can be read to an accuracy of 1°. Bearings should be taken on at least two prominent landmarks whose position on the map can be identified. To minimise errors the two landmarks should preferably be about 90° apart.

A correction has to be applied to each compass reading to allow for the difference between magnetic north and grid north on the map. As the amount of correction varies both with time and from one part of the country to another, it has to be calculated from data given on the map on each occasion and at every locality from which bearings are taken.

With the aid of a protractor the bearings are accurately drawn on the map. The point where they intersect marks the spot from where the readings were taken. Finally each outcrop is given a locality reference number. This is marked on the map and listed in the field notebook.

IDENTIFYING SPECIMENS COLLECTED IN THE FIELD

Guidance on the identification of the common minerals, fossils and rocks has been given in previous chapters. Very often in the field it is not possible to make a precise identification of a specimen at the time of collection. A fossil, for example, might be identified as a brachiopod, but a decision as to which particular brachiopod it is may have to wait until it can be examined in the laboratory and compared with other specimens and illustrations in the reference books.

It is important, however, that the locality where the specimen was collected is clearly marked on the map, that a brief description of everything seen and collected at that locality is recorded in the field notebook, and that a label bearing the locality reference number should be securely attached to the specimen before it is wrapped up and put away in the collecting bag. Just how the specimen should be labelled depends on its shape and size. Very small specimens might have to be put into numbered boxes. The point is that any specimen, be it rock, mineral or fossil, is useless to a field geologist unless it is known precisely where it came from and what else was found along with it.

TAKING MEASUREMENTS AT ROCK OUTCROPS

The next step, after identifying the rocks, is to examine the outcrops for structures which might provide clues to the geological history of the area. Structures to look for include the dip and strike of bedded rocks, faults, folds, cleavage, and joints. From these structures much can be learnt about the earth movements which the

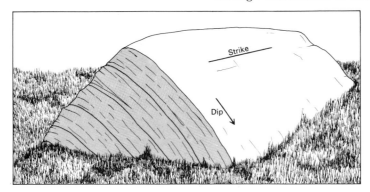

Figure 6.1   The relationship between the dip and the strike of an inclined bed.

rocks suffered after they had been formed. In sedimentary sequences the thicknesses of individual beds and groups of beds are important for comparison with beds of the same age in other areas. From cross-stratification and ripplemarks, details of the origin of the sediments and how they were deposited can be deduced. Similarly, by examining the detailed structure and field relationships of dykes, sills and other intrusive bodies, much can be learnt about the history of the igneous activity in an area.

The dip is the angle of inclination of a tilted bed and is measured in a downwards direction with a clinometer (Fig. 1.2). The strike of a bed is the direction at right angles to the direction of dip (Fig. 6.1). Both these directions are measured with a compass. If the surface of the exposed bed is smooth and regular, the clinometer is placed directly upon it when measuring the dip. Care has to be taken that the instrument is aligned along the direction of maximum slope of the bed. If the surface is irregular it is necessary to stand back from the exposure and, holding the clinometer at arm's length, match up its base visually with the general

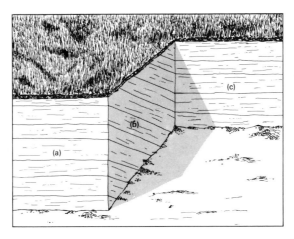

Figure 6.2   The relationship between the true and the apparent dip of strata: in faces (a) and (c) of the quarry the bedding appears to be almost horizontal, but in face (b) the true dip is seen.

63

dip of the bed. If possible, several readings should be taken and the average reading calculated.

Bedding exposed in cliffs, quarry faces and cuttings may not indicate the *true* direction and amount of dip, but show instead an *apparent* dip. This is because the exposure is cutting obliquely across the dip. The apparent dip is always less than the true dip. The extreme case arises when the exposure is running parallel to the strike of a dipping series of beds. In this situation the beds appear to be horizontal, when, in fact, they are dipping either directly towards or directly away from the observer (Fig. 6.2). For this reason, before any measurements are taken, a close examination of such exposures is always necessary in order to determine the true direction of dip. Careful measurements of the dip angles of the limbs of anticlines and synclines enable the hinge points of folds to be precisely located and traces of the axes of folds to be drawn on the map.

The forces which act on rocks subsequent to their formation can, if strong enough, fracture them and produce joints and faults. Joints are cracks which show no obvious displacement of the rocks, whereas faults are cracks where there has been measurable movement of the rocks on one side of the fracture relative to those on the other side.

The regular patterns shown by joints in brittle rocks lend themselves readily to measurement. Sedimentary rocks like limestone and sandstone often display several sets of joints. Usually they cut through the beds more or less at right angles to the bedding and when exposed on the surface of the bedding plane they form a criss-cross network of straight cracks. If compass readings are taken of the directions in which the cracks are running it is generally found that they can be grouped in two or three preferred directions. The joint pattern is often constant over a wide area.

The joints in sills, dykes, lava flows and other small igneous bodies are formed by contraction as the rocks cool down. Spectacular examples occur in many parts of Britain. In flat-lying sills and lava flows the joints produce nearly vertical, polygonal columns, but in dykes the columns run horizontally across from one wall to the other. In volcanic necks and other less regularly shaped igneous masses the polygonal jointing tends to develop a radiating structure (Fig. 6.3).

Dips can be measured on the surfaces of sills and lava flows in the same way as on the bedding planes of sedimentary rocks. With dykes the principal measurements are their width and the directions in which they trend. In sills and lava flows the thickness is measured perpendicular to the top and bottom surfaces as in the case of sedimentary beds (Fig. 1.1).

In rocks which have been faulted the main problem is to determine the throw (i.e. the amount of displacement) of the fault and the direction in which this movement took place. Small faults, if well exposed, present no great difficulty as the throw can easily be measured and the direction of movement is obvious (Fig. 1.3). Large faults, those with throws of tens or hundreds of metres, are, however, rarely seen at the surface since the rocks immediately adjacent to the fault, fractured and weakened by the movement, have subsequently been eroded to form low ground devoid of exposures. The positions of such faults have generally to be inferred from sudden changes in rock type or rapid alterations in the dip of stratified rocks in the vicinity of the fault.

64

Figure 6.3   Radial jointing in basalt at the Rock and Spindle volcanic vent near St Andrews, Fife.

In addition to taking measurements it is often necessary to keep a visual record of details of the outcrops in the form of photographs and sketches. If the lighting conditions are favourable, photography is more accurate but very often it happens that the most interesting part of an exposure lies in the shade of over-hanging vegetation, or it faces north, or the weather is overcast, or the colours of the rocks show insufficient contrast. In any of these circumstances an accurate sketch is more valuable than a photograph. Wherever possible, in both sketches and photographs, the scale should be indicated by the inclusion of some person or some familiar object, such as a hammer or a coin.

CONSTRUCTING THE GEOLOGICAL MAP

The next step, after completing the detailed examination of the outcrop, is to insert on the base map a summary of what has been found and measured. As space is limited the information has to be condensed, and shown partly in an abbreviated form and partly as symbols. The names of the common rocks can be shortened; sandstone, for instance, is written on the map as Sst, limestone as Lst, and basalt as Ba. The dip of a bed is commonly shown by a small arrow point-ing in the direction down which the bed is inclined, the tip of the arrow marking the exact spot at which the measurement of the dip was made. A horizontal bed is shown by a plus sign, and a vertical bed is indicated by a right angle cross with a long limb and a short limb, the long limb being aligned in the direction of the strike of the bed. A list of the common symbols used on geological maps is given in Table 6.1.

Table 6.1 *Symbols used on geological maps*

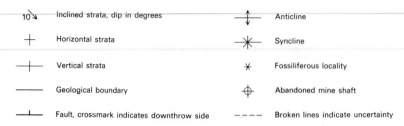

10↘	Inclined strata, dip in degrees	↕	Anticline
+	Horizontal strata	⚹	Syncline
┼	Vertical strata	✳	Fossiliferous locality
——	Geological boundary	⊕	Abandoned mine shaft
⊥	Fault, crossmark indicates downthrow side	----	Broken lines indicate uncertainty

In the field the various items of geological information are first pencilled on the map in very small, clear writing as the survey proceeds. Later, at the earliest opportunity after returning to base, the pencilled information is rewritten with waterproof drawing ink to provide a more permanent record. By systematically

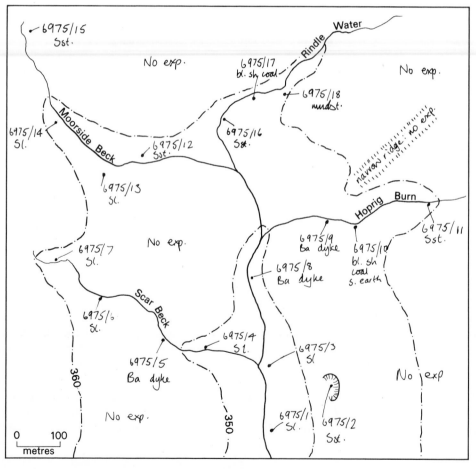

Figure 6.4 Field map showing the localities where rock exposures and topographic features were examined.

working over an area and examining every outcrop of rock, a map similar to that shown in the following example (Fig. 6.4) will gradually be built up.

The area is in an upland region at the head of a shallow valley which is drained to the south by the Rindle Water. Low, grass-covered hills and moorland lie to the east, north and west. The survey began at the southern edge of the area and the first outcrop was found on the east bank of the Rindle Water. A problem immediately arose due to difficulty in locating the exact position of this outcrop on the map. It was solved by going farther upstream, locating the junction of the main stream with the Scar Beck tributary and pacing out the distance back to the outcrop. This was found to be 135 metres. The locality was now plotted on the field copy of the base map and given a reference number, 6975/1, since it was the first outcrop examined on the day, which was 6th September, 1975. The rock was slate, indicated by the symbol, Sl, on the map. Details of the locality recorded in the field notebook were as follows:

Loc. 6975/1. E. bank of Rindle W., 135 m S. of j. with Scar Beck. 3·6 m blue-grey slate. One good cleavage dips S. at 87°. Bedding dips at 65° on bearing 183° from mag. N.

A second outcrop was found 150 metres to the north-east of the first. This was an abandoned sandstone quarry. Its position was already indicated on the base map and so there was no need to plot its position. The entry in the field notebook was as follows:

Loc. 6975/2. Old q. 155 m E.S.E. of j. of Rindle W. and Scar B. 2·8 m fine-gr., micaceous Sst w. shale partings. Part of *Calamites* stem in Sst. Dip approx. 20° to N.E.

A third outcrop of slate was located at 6975/3. The cleavage again was nearly vertical and the bedding inclined almost due south, but at the much lower angle of 34°. On proceeding up the Scar Beck tributary, slate appeared again about 125 metres upstream. It was grey and cubes of pyrite were scattered through it. This time the dip of the bedding was 38° in a direction 2° east of magnetic north.

At locality 6975/5 a basalt dyke, 1·7 m wide was seen to cross the stream. It was very fine-grained, non-porphyritic, with margins which were glassy for about 2 cm inwards. The trend of the visible portion of the dyke was 48° east of magnetic north. Farther upstream, at 6975/6 and 6975/7 grey slate was again exposed. In the first exposure the dip of the bedding was 68° to the north, the second was too weathered to allow precise measurement of the dip but it appeared to be similar to the first.

No further exposures were seen in the Scar Beck area, but, on returning to the main valley, a dyke of basalt was seen at 6975/8 cutting obliquely across the Rindle Water in a north-east direction. It was 1·9 m wide and the central 15 cm contained porphyritic feldspar crystals up to 8 mm long.

The next section to be surveyed was in the Hoprig Burn. Upstream, 160 m from the confluence with the Rindle Water, basalt was again exposed in dyke form. This time it was 1·8 m wide, slightly porphyritic, and trending 50° east of magnetic north. A further 60 m upstream the steep south bank had been undercut to expose 1·2 m of black shale overlying a seam of rather poor coal, 40 cm thick, which in turn was overlying a white, sandy seatearth containing many fossil rootlets. A search for fossils in the shale eventually produced some squashed and rather badly preserved ammonoids. The dip of the shale bed was 21° at 46° east of magnetic north. The only other exposure in the Hoprig Burn was another 170 metres upstream where 3·2 m of cross-bedded sandstone was seen. It was pale buff in colour and fairly coarse in grain.

On the hillside north of the Hoprig Burn there were no rock exposures, but it was noted that a narrow, upstanding ridge could be traced over the grass-covered hillside in a north-easterly direction.

The Moorside Beck section was now examined. At 6975/12, 215 m from the confluence with the Rindle Water, flaggy, ripple-marked sandstones were exposed in the bank of the stream. The strata were somewhat disturbed, so that it was difficult to measure the dip precisely, but it was about 45° and in a north-easterly direction. Farther upstream, at 6975/13 and 6975/14, the exposures were of slate again. The cleavage planes were still almost vertical and the dip of the bedding, measured in the first exposure at 52°, was nearly due south in direction. The last exposure in the Moorside Beck was at 6975/15 where 2 m of dark grey, micaceous sandstone with shale partings were seen to be dipping to the north-east with variable dips between 20° and 50°.

The final section of the area to be surveyed was the upper part of the Rindle Water valley. At 6975/16 a bed of massive, fine-grained, grey sandstone containing fossils recognised as the Carboniferous plant, *Stigmaria*, was seen. It was 3 m thick and the dip was about 25° to the north-east. Upstream 80 m there was a poor exposure of black shale on top of low quality coal. The shale was 1·2 m thick and, after prolonged digging and searching, some fragments of ammonoids were found in it. About 70 m upstream from the shale the final exposure was found. It consisted of unfossiliferous, grey mudstones. The dip was difficult to measure but was about 20° to the north-east.

This completed the activities in the field. On return to base the first job to be done was the inking in of the pencilled data on the field map. The second task was to convert the magnetic compass readings to bearings measured relative to grid north. Information printed on the base map indicated that in 1972 magnetic north was 6·5° west of grid north and decreasing about 1° in eight years. This meant that a deduction of 6° had to be made to every compass bearing to convert them to grid north bearings.

The information regarding the direction and amount of dip at each exposure where the dip could be measured was now transferred to a fresh copy of the base map. The outcrops of basalt were also plotted. When this was done several points became apparent.

The most obvious of these was the alignment of the three outcrops of basalt and the ridge on the hillside north of the Hoprig Burn. Bearing in mind the known behaviour of such dykes, it was reasonable to assume that most probably the dyke traversed the whole of the area from north-east to south-west, and so its course, where reasonably certain, was traced on the fair copy of the map (Fig. 6.5) as a solid black line. Its inferred, but unproved, continuation to the south-east

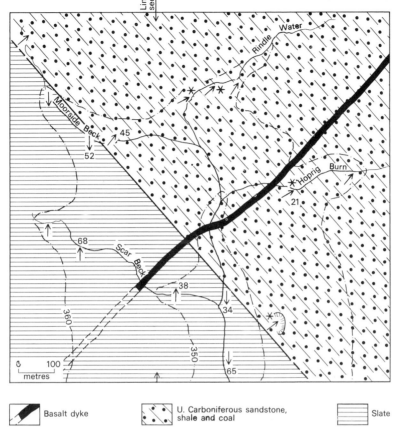

Figure 6.5   Completed geological map of the area shown in Figure 6.4.

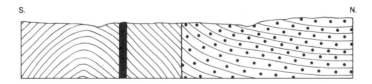

Figure 6.6   Section to show the geological structure of the area shown in Figure 6.5.

was shown as a broken line.

The second point to emerge was that there is an apparently fairly straight boundary between an area of slate in the south-west and one of Carboniferous sedimentary rocks in the north-east. The slate, being a low-grade metamorphic rock, is probably older than the unmetamorphosed Carboniferous rocks. The boundary could be either an unconformity or a fault, with a slight bias in favour of the latter in view of the disturbed nature of the sandstones in the Moorside Beck. A fault which runs from north-west to south-east was, therefore, drawn to separate the slate area from the sedimentary rocks. Mythical faults abound,

69

however, in geology, and this might well be another one. The possibility that the boundary is an unconformity remains a real one.

Laboratory examination of the ammonoids found at 6975/10 and 6975/17 revealed that they were goniatites of the Upper Carboniferous genus, *Gastrioceras*. The age of the rocks in which they were found was thus defined more precisely.

The final task of the survey was to draw a section across the completed map to illustrate the geological structure of the area. Figure 6.6 shows the section from north to south across the map.

The carrying out of a field survey similar to the one just described is generally not without its depressing moments, especially when done for the first time. There may be difficulty in recognising the rocks, exposures may be inaccessible, the rain will turn your field map into a soggy mess, you may fall in the stream and get your boots full of water, midges may make your life unbearable. In spite of this most people develop a taste for field-mapping and come to enjoy it. The beauty of fieldwork in geology is that one can never be absolutely certain of anything. There is always room for a different interpretation of the available evidence, as witness the inferred fault in the example quoted above. Fifty geologists given the task of mapping the same area would come up with fifty different interpretations, and who is to say which is the correct one? Your interpretation is likely to be just as good, or just as far-fetched, as any of the others. It might also be correct.

Appendix

WHERE TO GET MAPS AND GUIDES

Geological maps

A catalogue which lists the Geological Survey maps currently available can be obtained from the Ordnance Survey, Romsey Road, Maybush, Southampton SO9 4DH. Many of these maps can be purchased at the Ordnance Survey Agents and other stockists in most large towns. They can also be bought at the Bookshop in the Geological Museum, Exhibition Road, South Kensington, London SW7 2DE.

The libraries at the offices of the Institute of Geological Sciences in London, Leeds and Edinburgh hold very comprehensive collections of geological maps, ranging from early, out-of-print issues to the very latest publications, and these are available for public inspection. Those of Northern Ireland can be seen in the Institute's office in Belfast.

Excursion guides

The Geologists' Association publish a very useful series of local guides to the geologically important and interesting areas of Great Britain and Northern Ireland. The guides give details of the routes to be followed and an outline of the geological features to be seen. Information concerning these guides and copies of those available are obtainable from Messrs. Benham and Company Limited, Sheepen Road, Colchester, Essex.

Index